Contents

Introduction

The contents of this book are based upon the National Science Education Standards for Grade 3. These standards include (A) Unifying Concepts and Processes, (B) Science as Inquiry, (C) Physical Science, (D) Life Science, (E) Earth and Space Science, (F) Science and Technology, (G) Science in Personal and Social Perspectives, and (H) History and Nature of Science.

This book will help teachers, students, parents, and tutors. Teachers can use this book either to introduce or review a topic in their science classroom. Students will find the book useful in reviewing the major concepts in science. Parents can use this book to help their children with topics that may be posing a problem in the classroom. Tutors can use this book as a basis for their lessons and for assigning questions and activities.

This book includes nine lessons that focus on the nine major concepts presented in the content standards: Physical Science, Life Science, and Earth and Space Science. The lessons also cover the sixteen major concepts presented in the other standards. A table on page 4 provides a correlation between the contents of each lesson and the National Science Education Standards.

Before beginning the book, the reader can check his or her knowledge of the content by completing the *Assessment*. The *Assessment* consists of questions that deal with the content standards. This will allow the reader to determine how much he or she knows about a particular concept before beginning to read about it. The *Assessment* may also serve as a way of leading the reader to a specific lesson that may be of special interest.

Each lesson follows the same sequence in presenting the material. A list of *Key Terms* is always provided at the beginning of each lesson. This list includes all the boldfaced terms and their definitions presented in the same order that they are introduced in the lesson. The reader can develop a sense of the lesson content by glancing through the *Key Terms*. Each lesson then provides background information about the concept. This information is divided into several sections. Each section is written so that the reader is not overwhelmed with details. Rather, the reader is guided through the concept in a logical sequence. Each lesson then moves on to a *Review*. This section consists of several multiple-choice and short-answer questions. The multiple-choice questions check if the reader has retained information that was covered in the lesson. The short-answer questions check if the reader can use information from the lesson to provide the answers.

Each lesson then moves on to a series of activities. These activities are designed to check the reader's understanding of the information. Some activities extend the lesson by presenting additional information. The activities are varied so as not to be boring. For example, reading passages about interesting and unusual findings are included. Questions to check reading comprehension are then asked. As a change of pace, some activities are meant to engage the reader in a "fun-type" exercise. These activities include crosswords, word searches, jumbled letters, and cryptograms.

The last activity in each lesson is an experiment. Each experiment has been designed so that the required items are easy to locate and can usually be found in most households. Care has been taken to avoid the use of any dangerous materials or chemicals. However, an adult should always be present when a student is conducting an experiment. In some cases, the experimental procedure reminds students that adult supervision is required. Before beginning any experiment, an adult should review the list of materials and the procedure. In this way, the adult will be aware of any situations that may need special attention. The adult should review the safety issues before the experiment is begun. The adult may want to check a laboratory manual for specific safety precautions that should be followed when doing an experiment, such as wearing safety goggles and never touching or tasting chemicals.

The book then follows with a *Science Fair* section. Information is presented on how to conduct and present a science fair project. In some cases, the experiment at the end of a lesson can serve as the basis for a science fair project. Additional suggestions are also provided with advice as to how to choose an award-winning science fair project.

A *Glossary* is next. This section lists all the boldfaced terms in alphabetical order and indicates the page on which the term is used. The book concludes with an *Answer Key*, which gives the answers to all the activity questions, including the experiment.

This book has been designed and written so that teachers, students, parents, and tutors will find it easy to use and follow. Most importantly, students will benefit from this book by achieving at a higher level in class and on standardized tests.

National Science Education Standards Grades K-4

Standard A: UNIFYING CONCEPTS AND PROCESSES

A1 Systems, order, and organization
A2 Evidence, models, and explanation
A3 Change, constancy, and measurement
A4 Evolution and equilibrium
A5 Form and function

Standard B: SCIENCE AS INQUIRY

B1 Abilities necessary to do scientific inquiry
B2 Understanding about scientific inquiry

Standard C: PHYSICAL SCIENCE

C1 Properties of objects and materials
C2 Position and motion of objects
C3 Light, heat, electricity, and magnetism

Standard D: LIFE SCIENCE

D1 Characteristics of organisms
D2 Life cycles of organisms
D3 Organisms and environments

Standard E: EARTH AND SPACE SCIENCE

E1 Properties of earth materials
E2 Objects in the sky
E3 Changes in earth and sky

Standard F: SCIENCE AND TECHNOLOGY

F1 Abilities to distinguish between natural objects and objects made by humans
F2 Abilities of technological design
F3 Understanding about science and technology

Standard G: SCIENCE IN PERSONAL AND SOCIAL PERSPECTIVES

G1 Personal health
G2 Characteristics and changes in populations
G3 Types of resources
G4 Changes in environments
G5 Science and technology in local challenges

Standard H: HISTORY AND NATURE OF SCIENCE

H1 Science as a human endeavor

Correlation to National Science Education Standards

Unit 1: Physical Science

Lesson 1: Properties of Objects and Materials

Background Information A3, B1, C1
Review C1
All About Matter C1
Comparing Mass C1
Special Properties of Liquids C1, F1
Experiment: Investigating Gases B2, C1

Lesson 2: Position and Motion of Objects

Background Information A3, C2
Review C2
Position C2
Describing Motion C2
The Alaskan Sled Race C2, G5
Experiment: Investigating Motion B1, C2

Lesson 3: Light, Heat, Electricity, and Magnetism

Background Information A2, C3, F3
Review C3
Finding Forms of Energy C3
Heat Transfer C3
Electric Circuits C3
Experiment: Investigating Light A2, B2, C3

Unit 2 Life Science

Lesson 4: Characteristics of Organisms

Background Information A5, D1, F3
Review D1
Plant Parts A5, D1
Single-Celled Organisms A1, D1
Experiment: Investigating the
Needs of Plants A2, B2, D1

Lesson 5: Life Cycles of Organisms

Background Information A4, D2
Review D2
Growing Up D2
A Butterfly D2
The Emperor Penguin D2, G2
Experiment: Investigating the
Life Cycle of a Frog B2, D2

Lesson 6: Organisms and Environments

Background Information A1, D3, G2
Review D3
Forest Ecosystems D3
All About Environments D3
Organisms and Where They Live D3
Losing Ecosystems D3, G3, G4
Experiment: Investigating Environments. . B2, D3

Unit 3 Earth and Space Science

Lesson 7: Properties of Earth Materials

Background Information A2, E1, F1, G3
Review E1
Earth's Materials E1
Naming Earth's Materials E1
The Hawaiian Islands A4, E1, G4
Experiment: Investigating Soil B2, E1, G3

Lesson 8: Objects in the Sky

Background Information A1, E2, F1
Review E2
The Solar System E2
Finding Objects in the Sky E2
A New Way to Think About
the Solar System E2, H1
Experiment: Investigating Models A2, E2

Lesson 9: Changes in Earth and Sky

Background Information A3, E3
Review E3
Changes in the Sky E3
Seasons E3
Calendars A3, E3, H1
Experiment: Investigating Seasons A2, E3

NAME DATE

Grade 3 Assessment

Darken the circle by the best answer.

Lesson 1

1. Which state of matter has a definite shape and size?

Ⓐ solid

Ⓑ liquid

Ⓒ gas

Ⓓ mass

2. What is an atom?

Ⓐ the size of an object

Ⓑ the amount of matter in an object

Ⓒ a particle that makes up matter

Ⓓ the shape of an object

Lesson 2

3. You run down the street. What is your distance?

Ⓐ how fast you run

Ⓑ where you start

Ⓒ which direction you run

Ⓓ how far you run

4. Speed is distance divided by

Ⓐ mass.

Ⓑ time.

Ⓒ volume.

Ⓓ length.

Lesson 3

5. Heat is the movement of

Ⓐ matter.

Ⓑ light.

Ⓒ thermal energy.

Ⓓ electricity.

Lesson 4

6. The heart is an example of

Ⓐ an organ.

Ⓑ a cell.

Ⓒ a system.

Ⓓ an organism.

Assessment, page 2

7. Where do plants get energy for photosynthesis?
   Ⓐ wind
   Ⓑ water
   Ⓒ sun
   Ⓓ animals

Lesson 5

8. What happens when a seed germinates?
   Ⓐ It sprouts.
   Ⓑ It forms.
   Ⓒ It dies.
   Ⓓ It is blown by the wind.

Lesson 6

9. What does an energy pyramid show?
   Ⓐ Energy increases along a food chain.
   Ⓑ Energy stays the same along a food chain.
   Ⓒ All organisms in a food chain make new energy.
   Ⓓ Energy decreases along a food chain.

Lesson 7

10. What causes metamorphic rock to form?
   Ⓐ weathering and erosion
   Ⓑ volcanic eruptions
   Ⓒ high heat and pressure
   Ⓓ strong wind and rain

Lesson 8

11. How is the solar system arranged?
   Ⓐ the planets move around the sun
   Ⓑ the sun moves around Earth
   Ⓒ Earth moves around the moon
   Ⓓ the sun moves around the moon

Lesson 9

12. How long does it take for Earth to complete one rotation?
   Ⓐ 1 minute
   Ⓑ 1 hour
   Ⓒ 1 day
   Ⓓ 1 year

Lesson 1 Properties of Objects and Materials

Suppose you are visiting a zoo. Think about what you see there. You see animals. You see where they live and what they eat. What else do you see? Perhaps you see trees and other plants. You probably see other people there, too.

All of the things you see take up space. Anything that takes up space is **matter**.

Key Terms

matter—any material or object that has mass and takes up space

physical property—a characteristic of matter that can be found using the senses

solid—the state of matter that has a definite shape and takes up a definite amount of space

liquid—the state of matter that has definite volume but takes the shape of its container

gas—the state of matter that has no definite shape or size

atom—the most basic part of matter

volume—the amount of space an object or material takes up

mass—the amount of matter in an object

Physical Properties

When you look at the animals at the zoo, you learn a lot about them. You find out what they look like. Sometimes you get a chance to find out what they feel like. Many times you even know what they smell like!

Anything you can find out about something by using your senses is a **physical property**. When you use your senses, you see, touch, smell, taste, or hear something.

Seeing Matter One physical property of matter that you can see is color. You can tell the color of an object just by looking at it. A book might be blue. A pencil might be yellow.

When you look at an object, you can also tell if it is shiny or dull. A new penny might be shiny. An old spoon might be dull.

You can see if an object is big or small. You can also look at the shape of an object. A dish might be round. A shoelace might be long and thin.

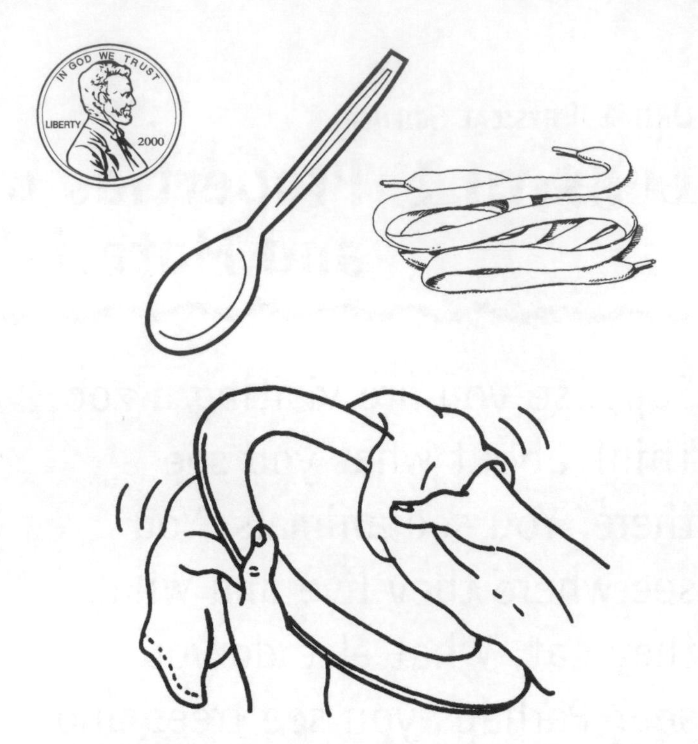

Feeling Matter When you touch an object, you can find out what it feels like. Your desk might be smooth and hard. A blanket might be soft. A fork might be pointy.

Different parts of the same object might feel different. The petals of a rose are very soft, but the thorns are sharp.

Smelling Matter Have you ever smelled bread baking in an oven? Do you know the smell of a freshly peeled orange? Most people like those smells. Many smells are pleasant. You often know right away what the smell is coming from.

Sometimes smells are not as pleasant. A piece of food that has gone bad makes a strong smell. So does a skunk. Most people do not like these smells. Good or bad, how something smells is one of its physical properties.

Tasting Matter What are your favorite foods? Are they sweet like an apple? Maybe they are salty like a pretzel. They might even be sour like a lemon. Your tongue can taste whether something is sweet, salty, sour, or bitter.

You can learn about foods by tasting them. If you taste other types of matter, you might get hurt. Some things can make you sick. You should never taste anything in your science classroom unless your teacher tells you that you should.

Hearing Matter If you listen carefully, you will hear sounds around you. You might hear a clock ticking. There might be an airplane flying in the sky. Perhaps a bird is chirping in a tree. Even if you do not see an object, you might know what it is by the sound it makes.

States of Matter

A seal at the zoo is one form of matter. The water it drinks and the air it breathes are different forms of matter. Matter has three different forms, or states. The three states of matter are solid, liquid, and gas.

Solids A seal is a solid. A **solid** takes up a specific amount of space and has a definite shape. If the seal moves from one place to another, it takes up the same amount of space. It still looks like a seal because its shape stays the same.

Liquids The water a seal drinks and swims in is a liquid. A **liquid** takes up a specific amount of space, but its shape can change. When you pour water into different containers, the amount of water does not change. The shape of the water does change. The water takes the shape of the container.

Gases The air a seal breathes is a gas. A **gas** does not take up a certain amount of space and does not have a definite shape. A gas takes the shape of its container. It spreads out to fill the entire container. Think about the air around you. There is not a part of the room that does not have air. Air fills the entire room.

Particles of Matter

Have you ever built a sand castle? When a sand castle is made, it looks like one solid thing. It is actually made up of millions of tiny grains of sand.

Just as a sand castle is made of smaller parts, so is all matter. The most basic parts of matter are **atoms**. Atoms are so small that they can only be seen using special tools. Sometimes atoms join together to form larger particles. Even these particles are very small.

There are many different types of particles. They determine the type of matter. All water, for example, is made up of the same particles. How the particles are arranged depends on the state of matter.

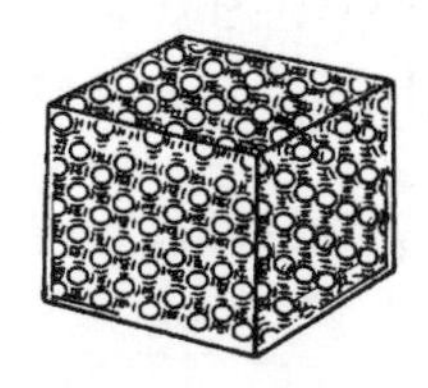

In a solid, the particles are close together. They do not move very much. They move only a little.

In a liquid, the particles move a little more than in a solid. They can slide past each other. This is why a liquid can flow.

In a gas, the particles can move a lot. They move fast in all directions. They bump into each other and into the walls of their container.

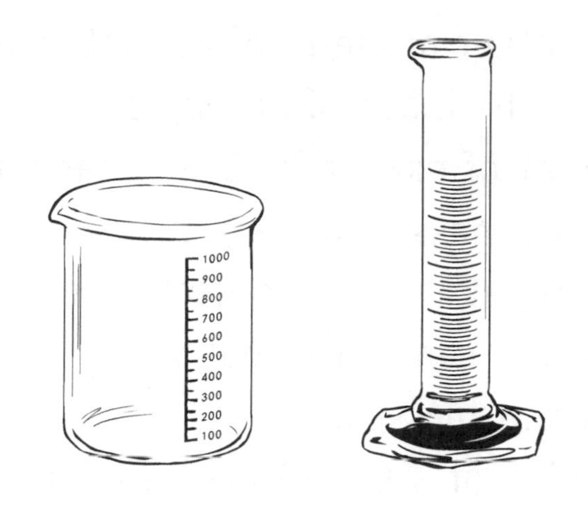

Measuring Matter

All matter takes up space. Some objects take up more space than others. A book takes up more space than a pencil. The amount of space matter takes up is called **volume**.

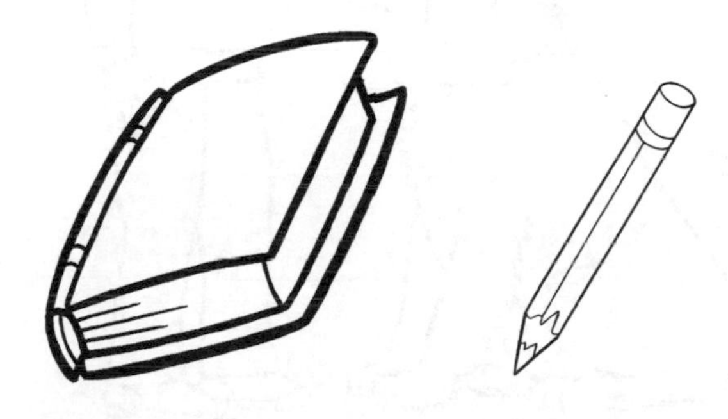

You have measured the volume of a liquid if you have ever used a measuring cup. Scientists use containers like a measuring cup to measure volume. The containers have lines that tell how much liquid is in the container. The lines are often broken into units called milliliters.

You can sometimes use a liquid to find the volume of a solid. Suppose you want to find the volume of a stone you found. You could add a liquid to a container. The marking next to the top of the liquid is its volume. If you place the stone in the liquid, the top of the liquid will get higher. The stone takes up some of the space in the container. The change in the top of the liquid is the volume of the stone.

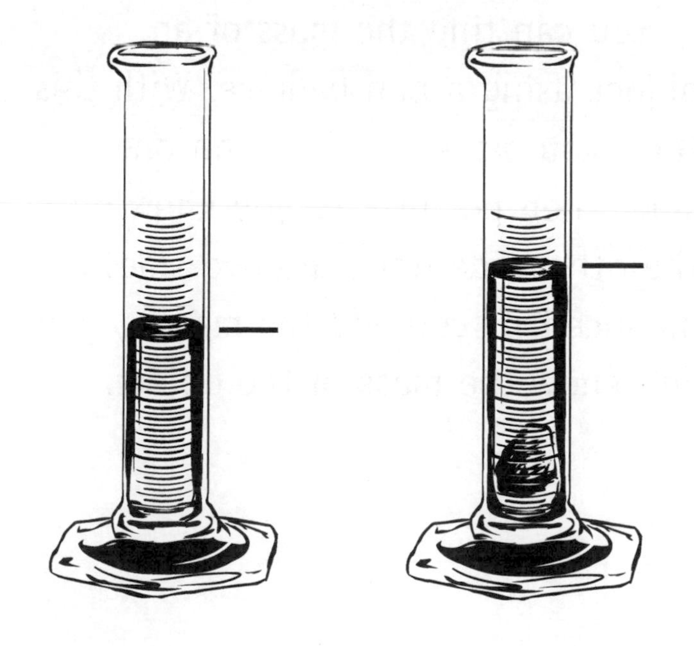

Another property of all matter is mass. The **mass** of an object is the amount of matter in it. You cannot tell the mass of an object just by looking at it. Some objects can have the same size, but very different masses.

Think of a box of marbles and a box of feathers. You can easily lift the feathers, but the marbles are a bit too heavy. That is because the mass of the marbles is greater than the mass of the feathers.

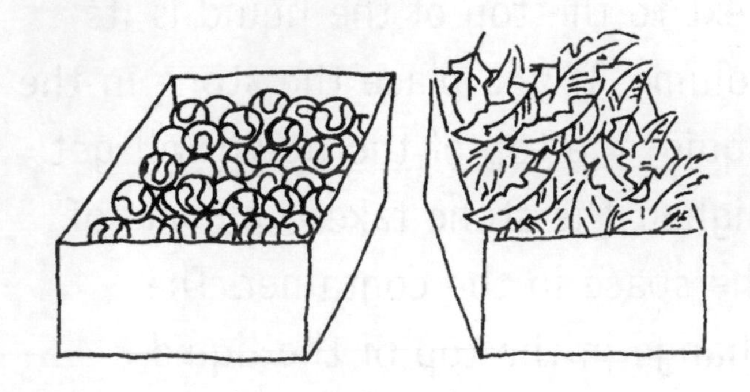

You can find the mass of an object using a pan balance. With this tool, you place an object on one side. Then put masses you know on the other side until the two sides are balanced. If you add the masses, you will know the mass of the object.

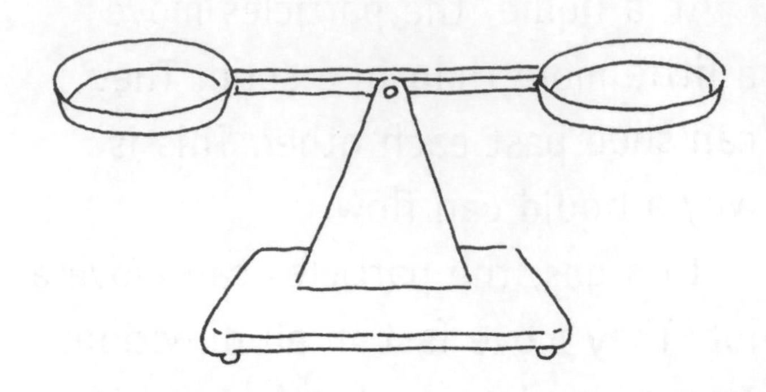

Mass is often measured in units called kilograms. The picture below shows the masses of some common objects.

dog
110 pounds
(50 kilograms)

third grader
66 pounds
(30 kilograms)

bananas
1 pound
(about 0.45 kilograms)

NAME DATE

Lesson 1

Review

Darken the circle by the best answer.

1. You can find all of these properties of a banana by seeing EXCEPT that it is
   - Ⓐ yellow.
   - Ⓑ sweet.
   - Ⓒ long.
   - Ⓓ bent.

2. Which sense do you use to find out that sandpaper is rough?
   - Ⓐ seeing
   - Ⓑ hearing
   - Ⓒ tasting
   - Ⓓ touching

3. Which part of your body do you mostly use to find out that a pretzel is salty?
   - Ⓐ nose
   - Ⓑ ears
   - Ⓒ tongue
   - Ⓓ fingers

4. Which state of matter takes up a definite amount of space but does not have a definite shape?
   - Ⓐ liquid
   - Ⓑ solid
   - Ⓒ gas
   - Ⓓ mass

5. What is the volume of an object?
   - Ⓐ how long the object is
   - Ⓑ how much space the object takes up
   - Ⓒ how much matter is in the object
   - Ⓓ what state of matter the object is in

6. What do you measure with a pan balance?
   - Ⓐ taste
   - Ⓑ color
   - Ⓒ mass
   - Ⓓ volume

NAME DATE

Review (cont'd.)

7. How are the particles of water different when it is a solid, a liquid, and a gas?

8. How is the mass of an object different from its volume?

NAME ____________________ DATE ____________________

Lesson 1

All About Matter

Write a key term to complete each sentence. Choose from the words below.

atom	gas	mass	physical	taste
balance	liquid	matter	solid	volume

1. You can use a pan ____________ to find the mass of an object.

2. Matter in the ____________ state will fill its container.

3. Every sample of ____________ has mass and takes up space.

4. You can use your senses to find the ____________ properties of an object.

5. A(n) ____________ is matter that has a definite shape and volume.

6. You use your sense of ____________ to find out that a lemon is sour.

7. The particles of a(n) ____________ can slide past each other.

8. The ____________ of an object tells how much matter is in it.

9. A(n) ____________ is the most basic part of matter.

10. The amount of space an object takes up is its ____________.

NAME DATE

Lesson 1

Comparing Mass

Look at each of the pan balances. Decide if one object has more mass than the other.

Write *A* if Object A has more mass. Write *B* if Object B has more mass. Write *Same* if both objects have the same mass.

______ 1.

______ 2.

______ 3.

______ 4.

______ 5.

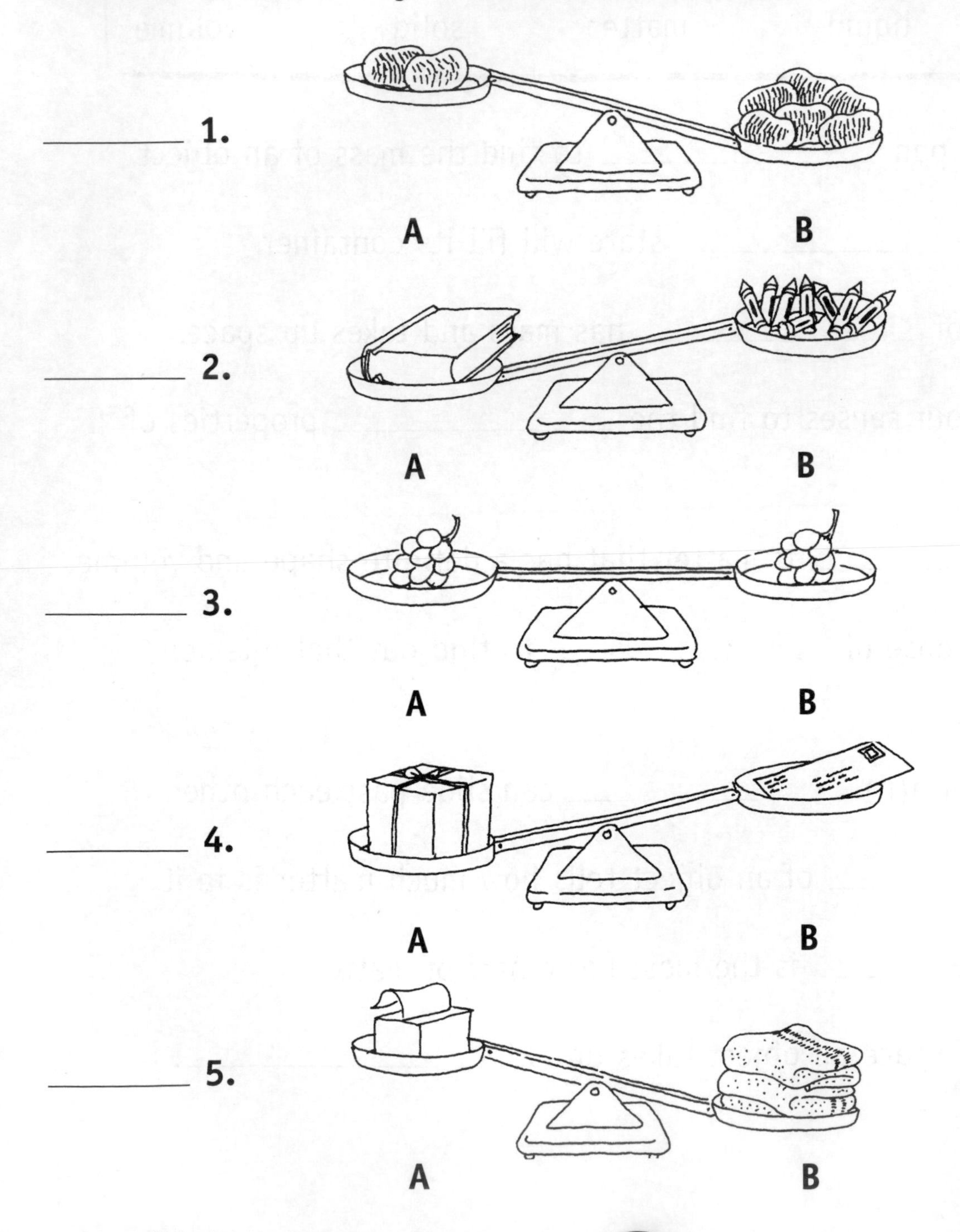

NAME DATE

Lesson 1

Special Properties of Liquids

Read the following passage. Then answer the questions that follow the passage.

Have you ever noticed a drop of water on a leaf? A special property of liquids is that they can form drops. Liquids form drops because they have something called surface tension.

To understand surface tension, think about a flat sheet of paper. Think about taping pieces of yarn along one side of the paper. If you pull the ends of the yarn to the same place, the paper will curl up. It is the same with liquids. The surface of the liquid is all pulled together. This causes the liquid to curl into a drop.

Sometimes there is too much water to form a drop. Then surface tension makes the surface of the liquid act like a thin skin. Small insects can walk on water in a pond for this reason.

Another special property of liquids describes how they flow. If you pour water into a glass, it flows quickly. If you pour honey into the same glass, it flows much more slowly than the water. Some liquids flow more easily than others.

1. Why do liquids form drops?

____

____

____

2. What property of water makes it possible for small insects to walk on it?

____

____

____

3. Molasses is a thick, sugary liquid. Do you think molasses will flow faster or more slowly than water?

____

____

____

NAME DATE

Lesson 1 Experiment: Investigating Gases

Like liquids and solids, gases take up space. It can be easy to forget this because you cannot see most gases. In this activity, you will prove that a gas takes up space.

What You Will Need

1 teaspoon of baking soda (about 4 grams)
2 tablespoons of vinegar (about 30 milliliters)
1.5 L plastic container (such as an empty soda bottle)
1 balloon
2 plastic spoons

Procedure

1. Stretch the mouth of the empty balloon open. Have a partner use a clean spoon to pour 1 teaspoon of baking soda into the balloon.
2. Use a clean spoon to pour 2 tablespoons of vinegar into the bottle.
3. Stretch the mouth of the balloon over the mouth of the bottle.
4. Lift up the end of the balloon so that the baking soda falls into the bottle. Watch what happens.

Analysis

1. When baking soda mixes with vinegar, they make a gas called carbon dioxide. Where did the gas go?

____

NAME DATE

Experiment: Investigating Gases (cont'd.)

2. What happened to the balloon?

Conclusion

Do gases take up space? How do you know?

Lesson 2 Position and Motion of Objects

A sailboat moves across the water on a windy day. A kite flies through the air. A dog runs across a field. All of these things are in motion. **Motion** is a change in position.

The position of an object tells where it is located. If the position changes, you know that the object is in motion. When you walk from the table to the refrigerator, you are in motion. When a bus drives from a house to the school, it is in motion.

Force

All types of motion are caused by a force. A **force** is a push or pull. When you kick a ball, your foot pushes the ball. Your foot applies a force.

A force is also what stops motion. When you want to stop your bicycle, you use the brakes. The brakes apply a force that stops your bicycle.

Once an object is in motion, it will move until a force changes it. Anytime you see a change in motion, you know that a force is involved.

motion—a change in the position of an object

force—a push or pull

speed—the distance an object moves divided by the time during which it moves

distance—the length an object moves from a starting position

Speed

Some objects move faster than others. A cheetah can move very fast. It can move up to 70 miles per hour. A snail moves much more slowly. It moves only 0.03 miles per hour.

The **speed** of an object measures how fast it moves over a certain distance. **Distance** is the length an object moves. A cheetah moves a greater distance in the same amount of time. The cheetah has a greater speed than the snail.

You can find the speed of an object if you know the distance it moves and how long it takes to move. Distance is measured in units of length. Miles and kilometers are two common units of length. Time is usually measured in seconds or hours.

Speed is the distance an object moves divided by its time. A certain train travels 195 miles in 3 hours. The speed of the train is 195 miles divided by 3 hours, which is 65 miles per hour.

A person running in a long race travels 24 miles in 4 hours. The person's speed is 6 miles per hour.

NAME ____________________ DATE ____________________

Lesson 2

Review

Darken the circle by the best answer.

1. What changes about an object when it is in motion?
   - Ⓐ its size
   - Ⓑ its position
   - Ⓒ its shape
   - Ⓓ its color

2. What does position tell you about an object?
   - Ⓐ where it is
   - Ⓑ what it is
   - Ⓒ how big it is
   - Ⓓ how fast it is

3. Which of these describes a force?
   - Ⓐ You look out the window.
   - Ⓑ You smell a flower.
   - Ⓒ You read a book.
   - Ⓓ You pull a wagon.

4. If one object moves faster than another, you know it has a greater
   - Ⓐ mass.
   - Ⓑ speed.
   - Ⓒ volume.
   - Ⓓ time.

5. Which of these is a measure of speed?
   - Ⓐ 2 hours
   - Ⓑ 2 miles
   - Ⓒ 2 objects
   - Ⓓ 2 miles per hour

6. How are forces related to motion?

   ____

   ____

7. What two pieces of information do you need to find an object's speed?

   ____

   ____

NAME ______ DATE ______

Lesson 2

Position

The pictures show several objects and their speeds. Number the objects in order of speed from slowest to fastest.

75 kmh (45 mph)

______

4 kmh (about 2 mph)

______

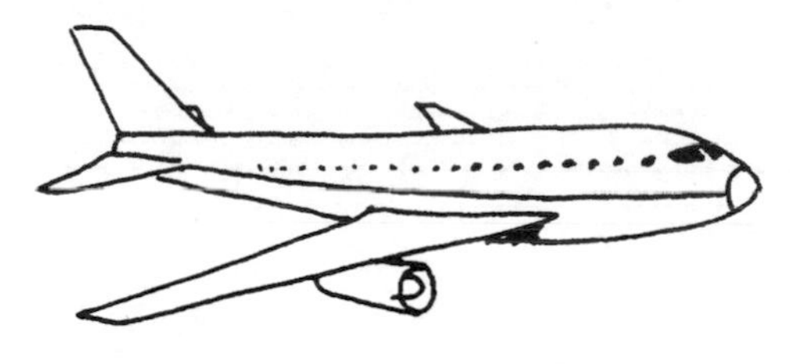

870 kmh (540 mph)

______

30,000 kmh (18,600 mph)

______

60 kmh (37 mph)

______

113 kmh (70 mph)

______

NAME DATE

Lesson 2

Describing Motion

The word *motion* is written below. Use each letter in the word to begin a sentence that describes motion. Be creative with your sentences. They can all describe different examples.

The first letter is done for you as an example.

My pet frog is hopping across the grass.

O ____

T ____

I ____

O ____

N ____

NAME DATE

Lesson 2

The Alaskan Sled Race

Read the following passage. Then answer the questions that follow the passage.

There is no other race like it in the world. Every year, a race begins in Anchorage, Alaska. For about two weeks, a team of dogs and a person called a musher race 1,049 miles to Nome, Alaska. The race is known as the Iditarod Sled Dog Race. The name of the race comes from the Native American word meaning "the distant place."

The racers move over some of the most beautiful land in the world. The conditions are tough. There are tall mountains, deep valleys, and frozen rivers. The racers pass thick trees and empty land. All of it is covered by snow and ice. The temperatures are below freezing and the wind is strong.

Racers travel at different speeds during the race. A dog team can move up to 30 miles per hour. They can't travel at those speeds for long, though. They run at speeds of about 11 to 12 miles per hour for most of the race.

The current record for the shortest time to finish the race is just over 8 days and 22 hours. The record for the longest time is 32 days!

The race has a long history. It began as a way to remember how the people of Alaska worked together to save lives. In 1925, the people of Nome were suffering from a disease called diphtheria. They needed medicine. Several teams of dog sleds carried the medicine as fast as they could. The trail they followed became the course of the race.

1. How is the meaning of the word *Iditarod* related to the race?

Ⓐ The sled teams use dogs.

Ⓑ The sled teams travel on snow.

Ⓒ The sled teams travel a great distance.

Ⓓ The sled teams move at high speeds.

NAME DATE

The Alaskan Sled Race (cont'd.)

2. What is one reason why the speed of the sled teams changes so much?

Ⓐ The rules say they have to slow down.

Ⓑ The conditions of the trail change a lot.

Ⓒ The sleds can travel only at low temperatures.

Ⓓ The teams can only speed up at the end of the race.

3. Which of these describes a length of time it might take the average sled team to finish the race?

Ⓐ 2 days

Ⓑ 14 days

Ⓒ 40 days

Ⓓ 100 days

4. How did the race begin?

Ⓐ as a way to carry visitors from one place to another

Ⓑ as a way to find the fastest dogs in the world

Ⓒ as a way to clear a path when a new city is built

Ⓓ as a way to remember how sled teams save lives

NAME DATE

Lesson 2 Experiment: Investigating Motion

When an object is in motion, its position changes. How fast its position changes depends on its speed. In this activity, you will find out how the speed of an object affects the time it takes to travel a distance.

What You Will Need

masking tape marker meter stick stopwatch

Procedure

1. Place a piece of masking tape on the floor. Write "Start" on it.
2. Use the meter stick to measure 6 meters. Place a second piece of masking tape on the floor. Write "End" on it.
3. Stand on the Start tape. Have a partner start a stopwatch and say "Go." When you hear this command, walk slowly to the End tape. Have your partner stop the stopwatch.
4. Write down how long it took you to move from the Start tape to the End tape.
5. Repeat steps 3 and 4, but this time walk at normal speed.
6. Repeat steps 3 and 4, but this time walk at fast speed.
7. Repeat steps 3 and 4, but this time jog.

Analysis

Walk	Time(seconds)
1	
2	
3	
4	

NAME DATE

Experiment: Investigating Motion (cont'd.)

1. What stayed the same each time?

2. What changed each time?

3. During which walk did you move the slowest? During which walk did you move the fastest?

Conclusion

According to your results, how does your speed affect the amount of time it takes you to move a certain distance?

UNIT 1 PHYSICAL SCIENCE

Lesson 3 Light, Heat, Electricity, and Magnetism

Have you ever jumped in puddles left behind by a rainstorm? Puddles only last for a little while. After the sun comes out, the puddles soon disappear. The reason is that the sun heats the water. The sun causes the puddle to change.

The ability to cause change is **energy**. There are many different forms of energy. The sun is the source of most of the energy on Earth. One important form of energy that comes from the sun is light. Light bulbs and fire are other sources of light.

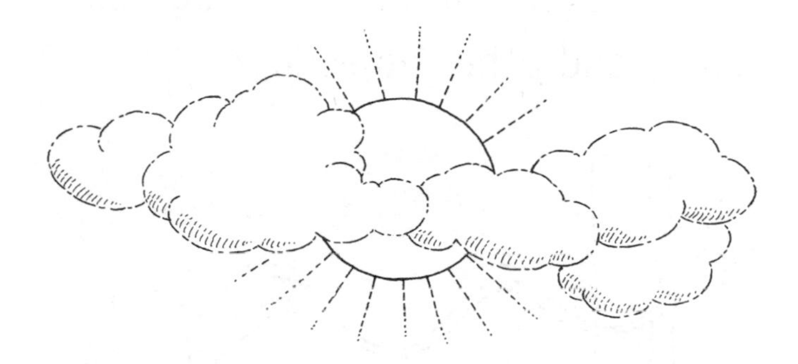

Key Terms

energy—the ability to cause change

thermal energy—the total energy of the particles in a sample of matter

heat—the movement of thermal energy from a warmer object to a cooler one

conduction—the flow of heat between objects that are touching each other

conductor—a material that lets thermal energy flow through it easily

insulator—a material that does not let thermal energy flow through it easily

convection—the movement of heat through liquids and gases

radiation—the movement of heat without the use of matter

battery—a device that stores electricity

circuit—a path through which electricity can flow

magnet—an object that pulls materials, such as metals with iron, to it

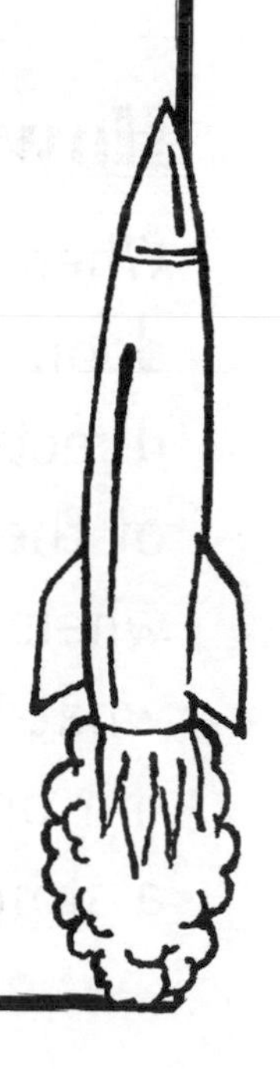

Light Waves

Light travels as waves. Think about attaching one end of a rope to a door knob. If you move the other end of the rope up and down, you make a wave. As the rope moves up and down, energy travels along the rope.

In much the same way, light energy travels as waves. Light does not need a rope or any other kind of matter. Light can move through air, space, and other objects.

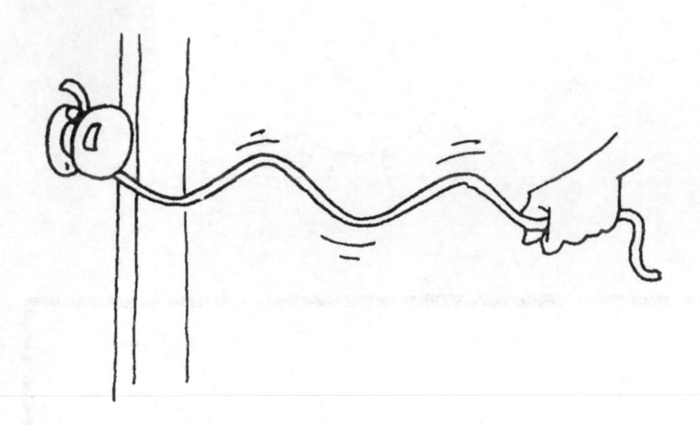

Some objects let most of the light that hits them pass through. This is how light can pass through a fish tank. If the light hits the object at an angle, it will bend. Some objects look bent or broken in water because of how light bends.

How Light Behaves

When the wave on a rope hits the door, it bounces back in the other direction. In the same way, some of the light waves bounce back when they hit an object. This is what happens when light hits a mirror. Light can also bounce off a shiny object like an apple.

Heat

Remember that all matter is made up of small particles that you cannot see. The particles are always moving. Moving things have energy. The energy related to the motion of particles of matter is called **thermal energy**.

The particles in an object move faster when the object is warm than when it is cold. The particles in hot chocolate move faster than the particles in cold chocolate milk. Hot chocolate has more thermal energy than the same amount of chocolate milk.

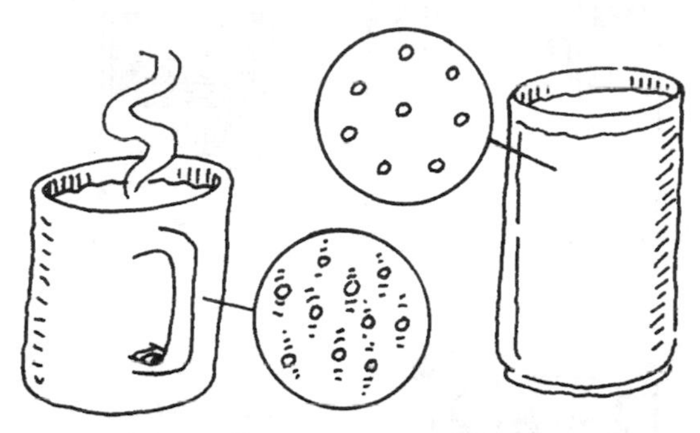

Thermal energy moves from a warmer object to a cooler one. If you put an ice cube in a glass of water, thermal energy moves from the warmer water to the cooler ice cube. The movement of thermal energy from one object to another is called **heat.**

Heat Transfer

Heat can flow from one object to another in different ways. These ways are known as conduction, convection, and radiation.

Conduction Heat can flow between objects that are touching. This type of heat transfer is known as **conduction**. Sometimes people heat metal in a fire. The metal heats up through conduction.

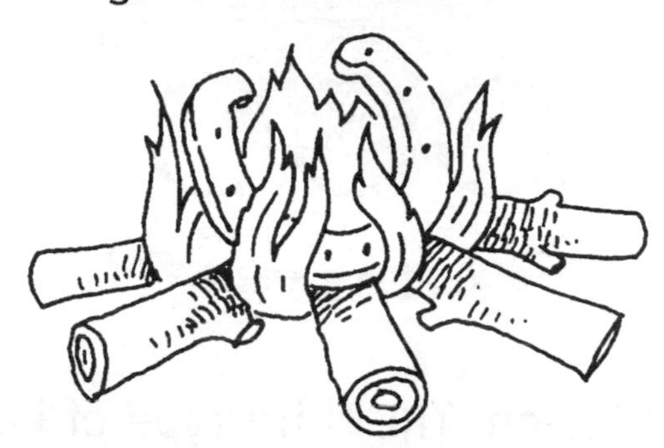

Thermal energy can move through some materials more easily than others. A material through which thermal energy can move easily is called a **conductor.** Pots and pans are made of metals because metals are good conductors of heat.

You don't want thermal energy to flow into your hand. This is why you hold a hot dish with an oven mitt. An oven mitt does not let thermal energy move through it easily. A material that prevents the flow of thermal energy is called an **insulator.**

Convection Heat can also move around in liquids and gases. This process is called **convection**. This type of heating is often used to heat the air in a room or an oven.

Convection also heats water in a pot on the stove. The air and the water move in a circle as they become heated.

Radiation The third type of heat transfer does not involve matter. The movement of heat without the use of matter is **radiation**. Heat flows from the sun to Earth by radiation. Energy from the sun warms you even though you are not touching the sun.

Electricity

Another type of energy is electricity. People make electricity from fuels such as coal and oil. They also make electricity from wind and moving water.

Electricity is then sent through wires to homes and businesses. You use this electricity when you put a plug into a wall socket.

Can you think of objects in your home that use electricity? Your refrigerator and lights use electricity. So do televisions, radios, and dishwashers.

Sometimes you may want to use electricity even when you are not near a wall socket. Many objects can use batteries instead. A **battery** stores electric energy until you need it.

You may know that batteries come in different shapes and sizes. A battery is filled with chemicals. Energy is stored in these chemicals. Batteries change this stored energy into electricity.

As a battery is used, the energy inside can be used up. Some batteries cannot be used again. Others can be recharged, or refilled with energy.

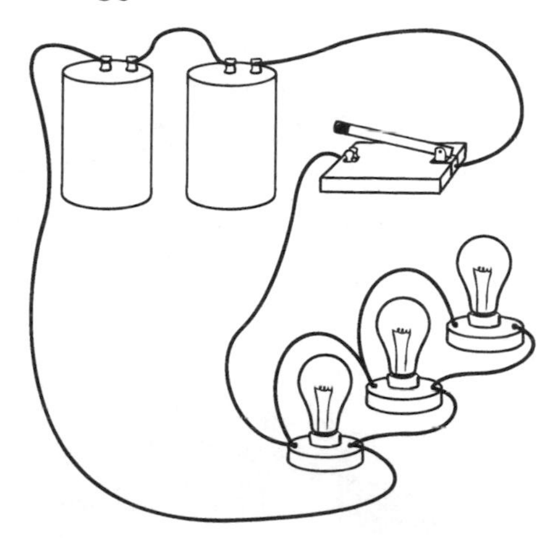

No matter where the electricity comes from, it must move through a path called a **circuit**. In a circuit, electricity flows from a source such as a battery. It flows to an object that uses electricity, such as a light bulb. It then flows back again. A switch turns the electricity on and off.

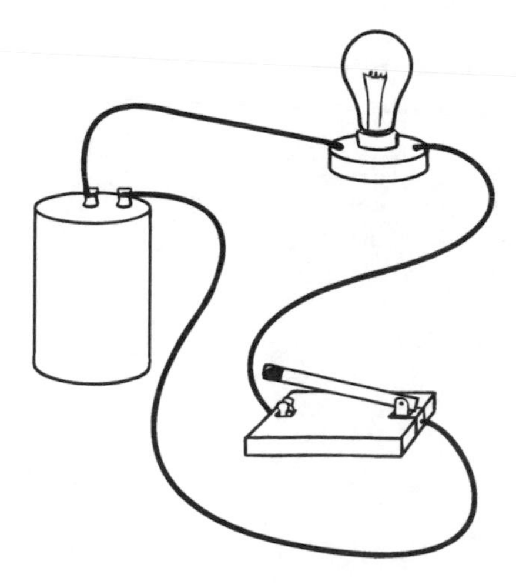

Magnets

Have you ever used a magnet? Maybe you have used a magnet to hold a sheet of paper on your locker. Perhaps you have toys that stay together because of magnets. Even your refrigerator door has a magnet that helps keep it closed.

A **magnet** is a type of matter that pulls objects containing iron. Many magnets are long and thin. These are called bar magnets. Others are shaped like horseshoes. Some magnets are even in the shape of a circle.

All magnets have two parts where the magnetic pull is stronger than anywhere else. These parts are known as the north pole and the south pole.

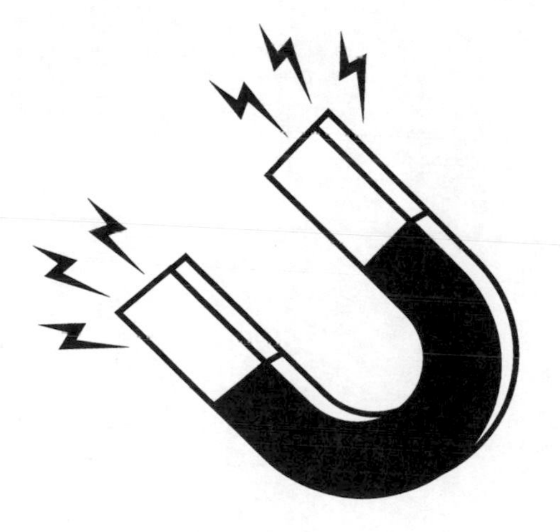

If the north pole of one magnet comes near the south pole of another magnet, the magnets pull together.

If two poles that are the same come together, they push each other apart. This means that if two north poles come near each other, they push each other apart. The same is true if two south poles come near each other.

NAME DATE

Lesson 3

Review

Darken the circle by the best answer.

1. What is energy?

Ⓐ a push or a pull
Ⓑ a state of matter
Ⓒ the ability to cause change
Ⓓ a type of particle

2. How does light travel?

Ⓐ It moves as a wave.
Ⓑ It moves as a cloud.
Ⓒ It moves in circles.
Ⓓ It shakes back and forth.

3. What happens to light when it hits a mirror?

Ⓐ It passes through.
Ⓑ It gets stronger.
Ⓒ It disappears.
Ⓓ It bounces back.

4. Thermal energy is most directly related to

Ⓐ an electric circuit.
Ⓑ the motion of particles of matter.
Ⓒ the poles of a magnet.
Ⓓ the bending of light.

5. How does heat get to Earth from the sun?

Ⓐ conduction
Ⓑ convection
Ⓒ radiation
Ⓓ It is passed from one particle to the next.

6. What does a battery do?

Ⓐ It makes chemicals.
Ⓑ It pulls metals with iron to it.
Ⓒ It lights up.
Ⓓ It stores electric energy.

NAME DATE

Review (cont'd.)

7. How does the motion of the particles of water change when it is heated?

8. How can magnets be used to hold a door shut?

NAME ______________________________ DATE ______________________________

Lesson 3

Finding Forms of Energy

Circle the following words in the puzzle below. They may appear horizontally, vertically, or diagonally.

BATTERY	CONDUCTION	ELECTRICITY	INSULATOR	POLE	THERMAL
CIRCUIT	CONVECTION	HEAT	MAGNET	RADIATION	WAVE

M	R	N	N	E	L	E	C	T	R	I	C	I	T	Y
A	O	E	O	C	I	R	C	U	I	T	N	E	R	R
G	T	G	I	I	E	Y	I	S	T	H	B	E	A	A
N	A	B	T	I	T	V	L	I	T	Y	A	H	T	D
E	L	O	C	T	C	C	A	A	U	S	T	E	E	I
T	U	C	U	H	H	A	E	W	N	G	T	A	E	A
H	S	M	D	F	M	E	T	V	V	K	E	T	O	T
Y	N	F	N	N	S	J	R	P	N	T	R	E	Y	I
I	I	A	O	X	F	K	P	M	C	O	Y	F	S	O
T	N	H	C	T	D	H	O	M	A	T	C	A	V	N
W	W	B	R	O	H	P	A	Z	Q	L	W	O	R	F
M	T	A	P	J	H	E	E	C	D	M	E	M	Y	I
E	E	H	O	A	F	L	I	Z	G	D	G	J	W	L
D	Y	Z	S	X	G	O	X	I	O	O	Y	K	F	L
G	X	C	Z	A	Y	P	C	D	C	Z	G	H	I	V

Underline the first 31 letters not circled. Write letters on the lines below the puzzle until you spell out a secret message.

_ _ _ _ _ _ _   _ _   _ _ _   _ _ _ _ _ _ _ _ _ _   _ _

_ _ _ _ _   _ _ _ _ _ _ _ _.

NAME DATE

Lesson 3

Heat Transfer

Each of the diagrams shows an example of how heat is transferred. Write <u>conduction</u>, <u>convection</u>, or <u>radiation</u> to tell the type of heat transfer shown.

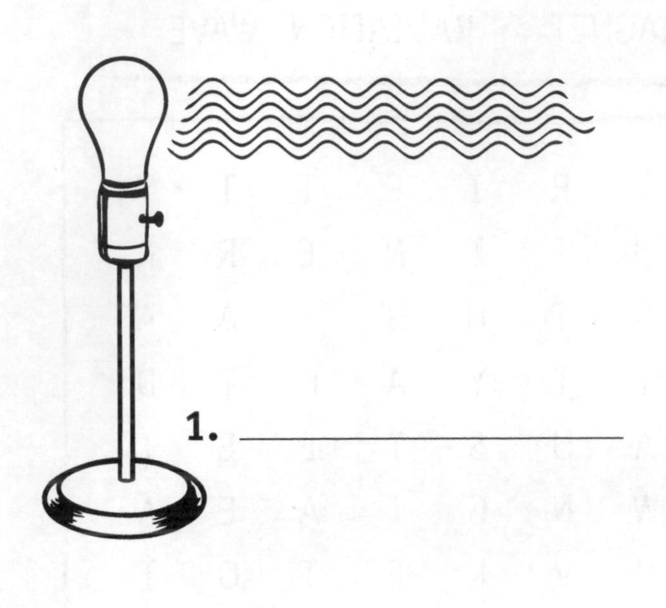

1. ____________________

2. ____________________

3. ____________________

NAME ______________________ DATE ______________________

Lesson 3

Electric Circuits

The diagram below shows an electric circuit. Look at the circuit. Then answer the questions below.

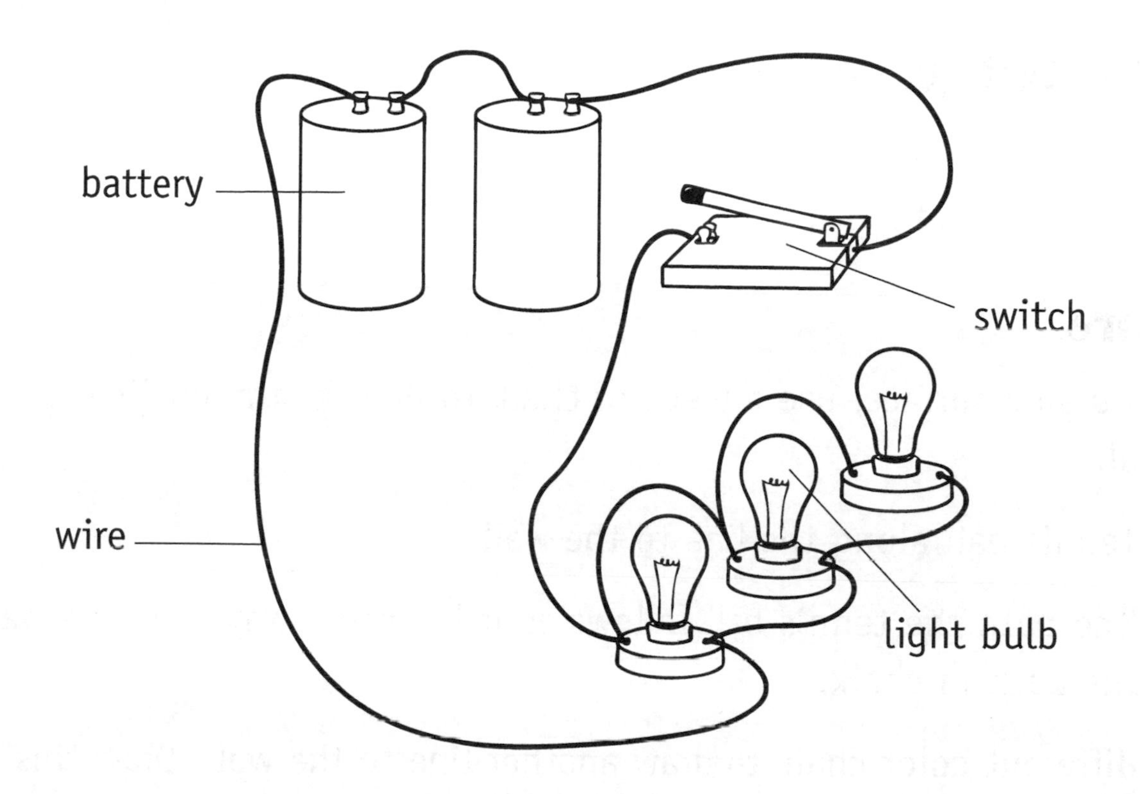

1. What is the source of electric energy?

____

2. What is the object that is powered by the electric current?

____

3. What does the electric current flow through to get to the light bulb?

____

4. How is the light turned on and off?

____

NAME DATE

Lesson 3 Experiment: Investigating Light

Is there any way to predict the direction in which light will bounce off a surface? In this experiment, you will find out.

What You Will Need

tennis ball	several colors of chalk
wall	meter stick

Procedure

1. On an outside surface, use a piece of chalk to draw a straight line to a wall.
2. Roll a tennis ball along the line to the wall.
3. Watch the path the tennis ball follows as it bounces away from the wall. Draw this path in chalk.
4. Use a different color chalk to draw another line to the wall. Draw this line at a slant to the wall. Repeat steps 2 and 3.
5. Repeat step 4 at different slants to the wall.

Analysis

In the space below, draw a diagram showing the lines to and from the wall.

NAME DATE

Experiment: Investigating Light (cont'd.)

Conclusion

1. In what direction does the ball bounce off the wall if it is rolled straight at the wall?

2. Does the ball bounce back in a different direction if the ball hits the wall at a slant?

Lesson 4 Characteristics of Organisms

You are surrounded by living things. You and your classmates are living things. Animals and plants are living things. Another name for a living thing is an **organism**.

Something that is not alive is called nonliving. Rocks, toys, and furniture are nonliving things. They do not have the same characteristics and needs of living things. They do not grow and change.

You will first look at the characteristics and needs of plants. Then you will find out about the characteristics and needs of animals.

Plant Structure

There are many different kinds of plants. Some are very large, such as tall redwood trees. Others are very small, such as the grass you walk on.

Most plants have the same basic parts. One plant part is underground. These are the roots. The roots take

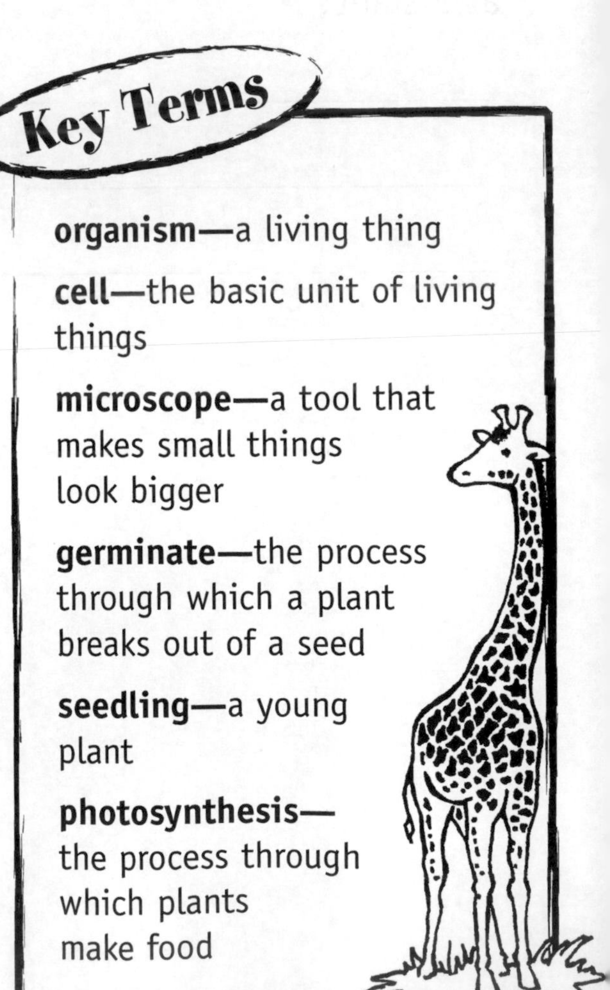

Key Terms

organism—a living thing

cell—the basic unit of living things

microscope—a tool that makes small things look bigger

germinate—the process through which a plant breaks out of a seed

seedling—a young plant

photosynthesis—the process through which plants make food in water and other things that the plant needs from the soil. The roots also hold the plant in the ground.

The roots are connected to the stem. The stem holds up the rest of the plant, such as the flowers and leaves. The stem carries materials from the roots to the rest of the plant. Some stems are thin and green. Others are thick and woody.

The leaves are the parts that grow out of the stem. Leaves take in air and light. Some plants have a few leaves. Other plants have many leaves. Plants make food in leaves.

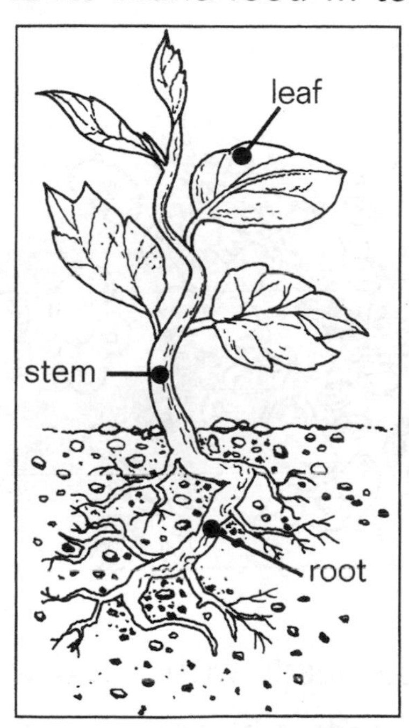

Leaves come in different shapes and sizes. Some leaves are wide and flat. Others are small and thick. Some leaves have smooth edges. Others have rough edges.

Some plants do not have roots, stems, and leaves. These plants are often called simple plants. A moss is an example of a simple plant. These types of plants take in the things they need directly from the environment. They do not have structures to carry materials from one part to another. As a result, they stay small.

Plant Cells

Just as matter is made of smaller particles, living things are made up of cells. A **cell** is the basic unit of life. Plants, like all living things, are made of cells.

Different cells have different jobs. A cell in a leaf helps the plant make food. A cell in a root helps the plant take in materials from the soil. All the cells in a plant work together to keep the plant alive.

Most cells are too small to see with your eye. Scientists use a tool called a microscope to see cells. A **microscope** makes small things look bigger.

Each cell has smaller structures inside it. These structures do jobs in the cell. The picture shows some of these structures.

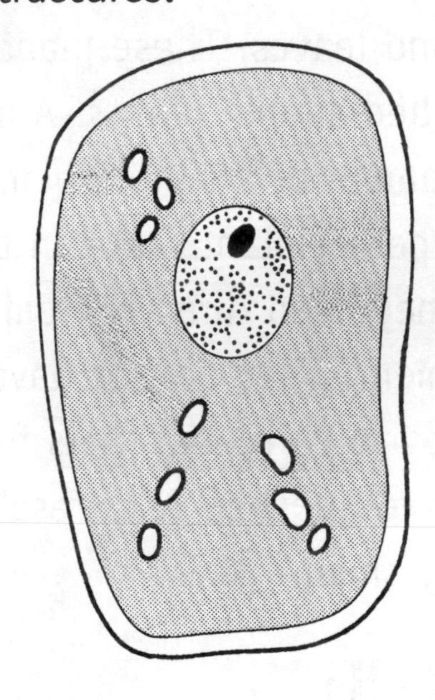

Plant Seeds

Simple plants do not make seeds. Some larger plants do not use seeds either. They use structures called spores to make new plants. You may have seen small circles on the bottom of fern leaves, or fronds. These are spores.

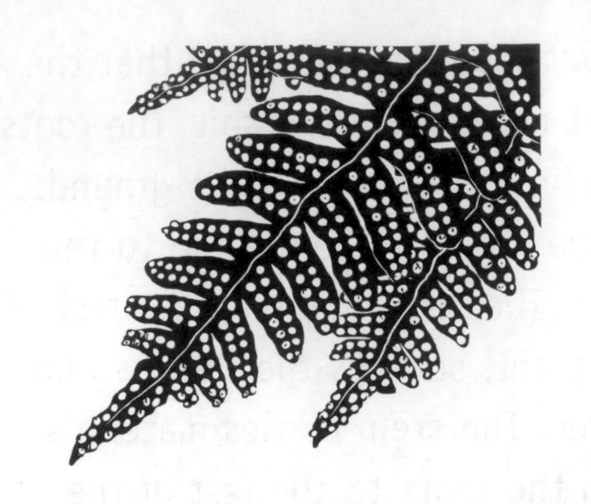

The first stage of growth for many plants is a seed. Some seeds are large, while others are small. Seeds can be round, pointed, or oval. There is a tiny plant in each type of seed. The plant is protected by a seed coat. There is food in the seed for the plant.

A seed needs water and warmth. It also needs soil and air. If the seed gets the things it needs, the small plant will break out of the seed. In other words, the seed **germinates**.

The seed then begins to sprout. When this happens, a root grows from the seed. Soon a young plant, or a **seedling**, appears. The seedling will grow into an adult plant. The new plant will look like the plant that made the seed.

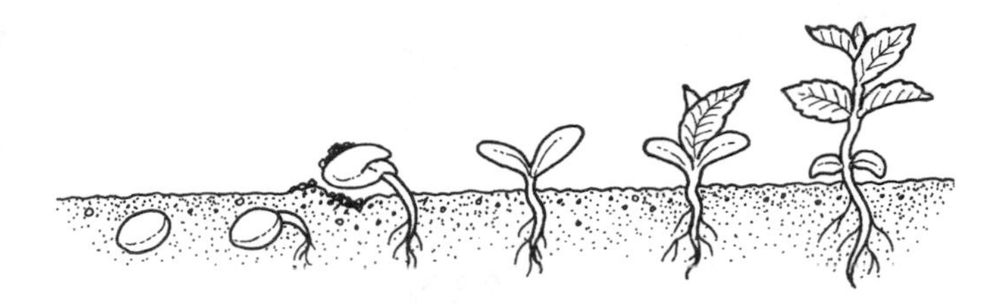

Forming Seeds

Some plants that use seeds make flowers. The seeds are made in the flowers. The male part of the flower is called the stamen. The female part is called the pistil. Pollen from the stamen lands on the pistil. This causes seeds to form. A fruit grows around the seeds.

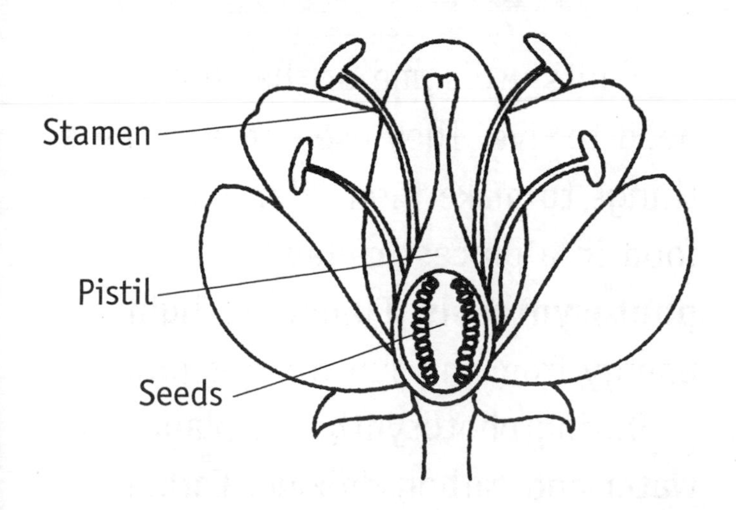

Not all plants that use seeds make flowers. Some plants make cones. A pine tree makes cones. There are two kinds of cones. The male cone is small and the female cone is large. Seeds form when pollen from the male cone reaches the female cone.

The cones have hard scales. When the seeds are ready, the scales open and let the seeds out.

Spreading Seeds

Most plants make many seeds. Not all of the seeds will land in a place where they can sprout. Plants need to spread their seeds so as many plants as possible can grow.

Some seeds, such as mangrove seeds, can float and can be carried by water.

Other seeds, such as milkweed, are light enough to be carried by the wind.

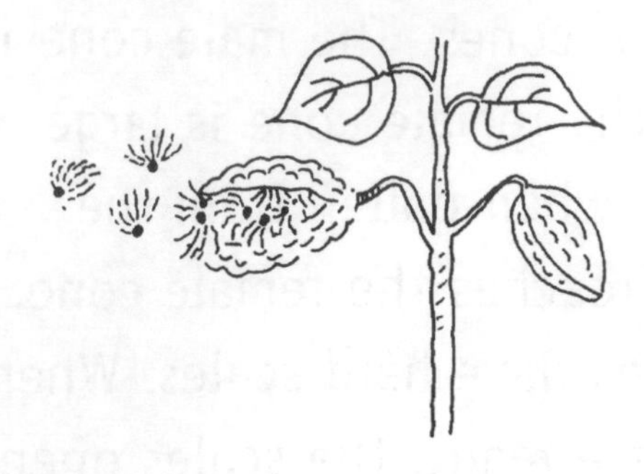

Seeds such as cocklebur s have hooks. They hook onto animals or people. They are then carried to new places.

Do you know how sweet fruits help plants grow? The sweet taste of fruits attracts animals. The animals eat the fruits and the seeds inside. The seeds pass through the animals and are dropped in new places as waste.

The Needs of Plants

As you may have guessed by now, plants need water and light. They also need soil and air. Some plants need a lot of water. Mangrove trees that live in swamps grow well in water.

Other plants can live with only a little water. Cactus plants live in deserts that do not get much rain.

Plants use some of the things they need to live. They use some of these things to make food. Plants make food in a process called **photosynthesis**. Plants use light energy from the sun for this process.

During photosynthesis, plants use water and carbon dioxide. Carbon dioxide is a gas in the air. Plants make food in the form of sugar. They use some of this food to give them the energy they need to live. They store the rest in their roots, stems, and leaves. They also make a gas called oxygen.

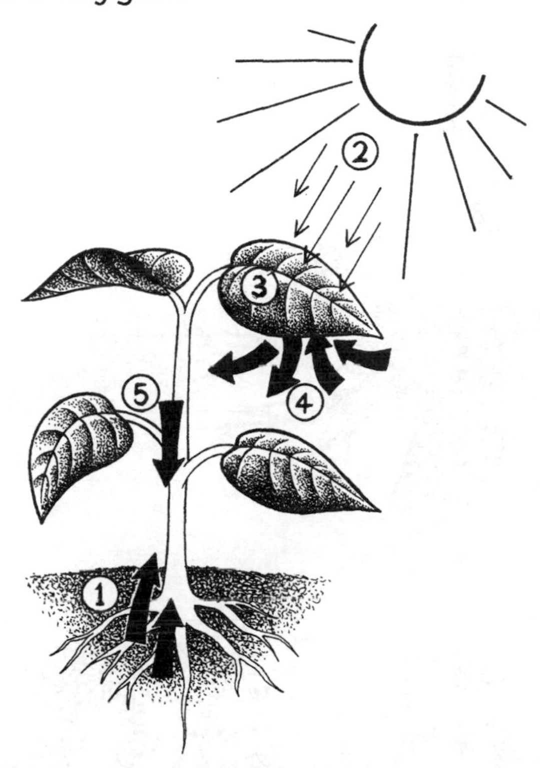

Follow these steps in the picture above.

1. Plants take in water from the soil.
2. Plants take in light energy from the sun.
3. Plants make food in their leaves.
4. Plants take in carbon dioxide and release oxygen.
5. Plants store sugar in their stems, roots, and leaves.

Animals

Animals have many of the same needs as plants. One important need is air. Animals need oxygen from the air. They use the oxygen that plants make during photosynthesis.

Animals that live on land, such as koala bears, use lungs to breathe air. Some animals, such as fish, get their oxygen from the water. Other animals that live in the water must come to the surface for air. Whales and dolphins do this.

Like plants, animals also need water. The bodies of animals contain water. Animals need water to keep cool. They also need water to carry materials inside their bodies.

Animals get much of their water by drinking it. They even get water in the foods they eat. Some animals get most of their water from foods.

Animals cannot make food the way plants can. To get energy, animals need to eat food. The food also gives animals materials they need to live.

Some animals eat plants. When they do, they get the food stored in the plants. They use some of the food to live, and they store the rest. Other animals eat animals. These animals get the food stored in the animals. Some animals eat both plants and animals for food.

Just as plants need a place to grow, animals need a place to live. For animals, a place to live is shelter. A shelter protects animals from the weather. It also protects them from other animals.

Some animals, such as birds, build nests in trees. Squirrels might live in holes in trees. Foxes dig out holes in the ground to live in. Prairie dogs dig out long tunnels. Bears sleep in caves.

Animal Cells

Just as plants are made up of cells, so are animals. The cells do different jobs, but they work together to keep the animal alive.

NAME DATE

Lesson 4

Review

Darken the circle by the best answer.

1. What is a cell?

Ⓐ the most basic unit of life

Ⓑ the process through which plants make food

Ⓒ a type of plant that makes cones

Ⓓ a type of animal that eats plants

2. Which of these is a characteristic of all living things?

Ⓐ They are green.

Ⓑ They can move.

Ⓒ They make sounds.

Ⓓ They are made of cells.

3. In which structure does a plant make food?

Ⓐ root

Ⓑ stem

Ⓒ leaf

Ⓓ soil

4. Why do some plants make spores?

Ⓐ to make food

Ⓑ to reproduce

Ⓒ to eat other plants

Ⓓ to make flowers

5. What is the purpose of a cone in a pine tree?

Ⓐ to make food

Ⓑ to make flowers

Ⓒ to make seeds

Ⓓ to hold the tree in the ground

6. Which of the following materials do animals need from air?

Ⓐ carbon dioxide

Ⓑ food

Ⓒ oxygen

Ⓓ energy

NAME DATE

Review (cont'd.)

7. How do animals help carry plant seeds to places where they can germinate?

8. Why is shelter important to animals?

NAME DATE

Lesson 4

Plant Parts

The picture shows a plant. Write the name of each part of the plant. Use the words in the box below.

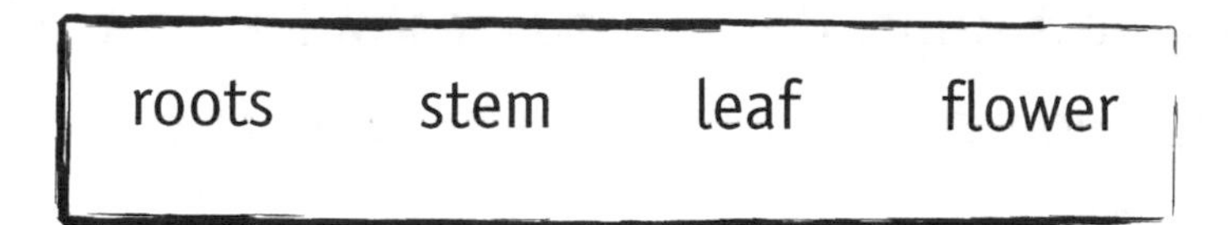

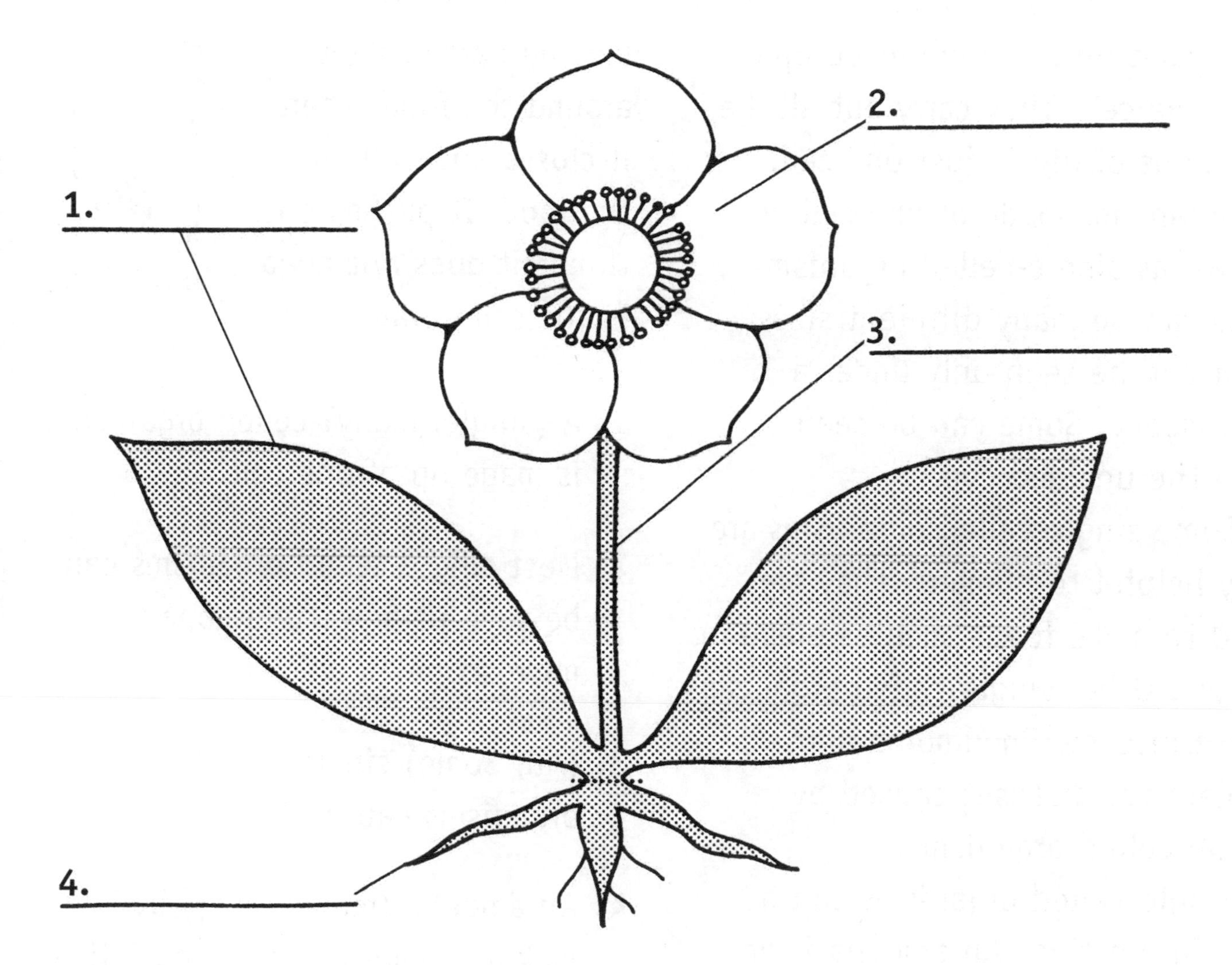

NAME DATE

Lesson 4 Single-Celled Organisms

Read the following passage. Then read the sentences that follow. Underline the word that correctly completes the sentence.

When you think of living things, do you think big? Perhaps you think of people, lions, tigers, and bears. You might be surprised to learn that most organisms on Earth are made up of only one cell. They carry out all the functions of life in just one cell.

Organisms made of one cell are known as single-celled organisms. They can be many different sizes. Most can be seen only under a microscope. Some can be seen with the unaided eye.

Some single-celled organisms are very helpful to humans. They are used to make foods such as bread or yogurt. Other single-celled organisms cause disease. Pneumonia and cholera are diseases caused by single-celled organisms.

Single-celled organisms can be very interesting. An amoeba is an example of such an organism. An amoeba moves and eats by changing the shape of its body. To move, it pushes out a part of the cell to look like a foot. Then it pulls the rest of the cell with it.

An amoeba takes in food by moving part of itself around the food. Then it closes and pulls in the food. It pushes out things it does not need in the same way.

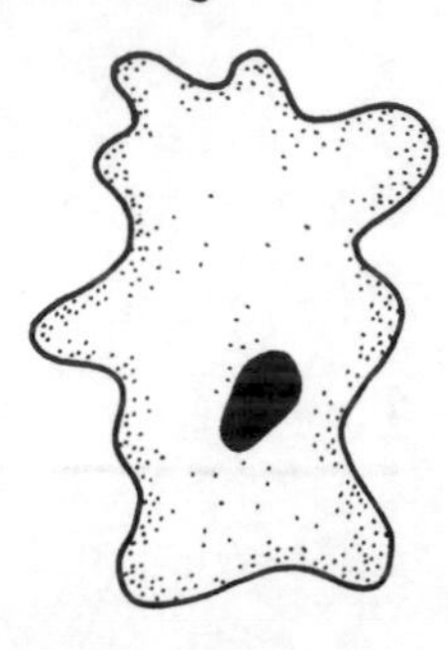

1. A (single, many)-celled organism is made up of one cell.

2. Most single-celled organisms can be seen using a (telescope, microscope).

3. (All, Some) single-celled organisms cause disease.

4. An amoeba (moves, eats) by making something that looks like a foot.

NAME DATE

Lesson 4

Experiment: Investigating the Needs of Plants

You need to eat food and drink water. Plants also have needs. In this activity, you will investigate some of these needs.

What You Will Need

3 small potted plants or seedlings
water
sunlight
ruler
marker
masking tape

Procedure

1. Use the marker to make the following labels on pieces of masking tape: "Plant 1—No Sunlight," "Plant 2—No Water," and "Plant 3—Control." Tape one label on each pot.
2. Measure the heights of the plants. Write down your measurements.
3. Put Plant 1 in a closet or other place where it will not get any light.
4. Put Plants 2 and 3 in a place where they will get some sunlight during the day.
5. Water Plant 1 and Plant 3 each day. Do not water Plant 2.
6. Write down how the plants look.
7. After 10 days, measure the heights of the plants again. Write down your measurements. Also write down how the plants look.

NAME DATE

Experiment: Investigating the Needs of Plants (cont'd.)

Analysis

Plant	Starting Height	How Plant Looks	Ending Height	How Plant Looks
1—No Sunlight				
2—No Water				
3—Control				

1. Why did you include a control plant?

2. What two things did you change in this experiment?

Conclusion

Can a plant grow without water or sunlight? Give reasons for your answer.

Lesson 5 Life Cycles of Organisms

Have you ever seen a baby animal? If you have, you know that living things grow over time. As they grow, they change in how they look and what they do. The changes that happen from the time an organism is born until it dies are known as its **life cycle**.

In Lesson 4, you saw how plants change. Many plants begin as seeds. Once the seed germinates, a tiny seedling starts to grow. If the seedling gets the things it needs, it grows and changes until it forms an adult plant. Animals also change and grow.

Metamorphosis

The life cycle of some organisms is described as metamorphosis. During **metamorphosis**, an organism changes in structure. Sometimes it even moves to live in a different place. One organism that undergoes metamorphosis is a frog.

Frogs begin as eggs released into water. The eggs hatch into tadpoles. Tadpoles have gills. The gills let the tadpoles take in oxygen from the water.

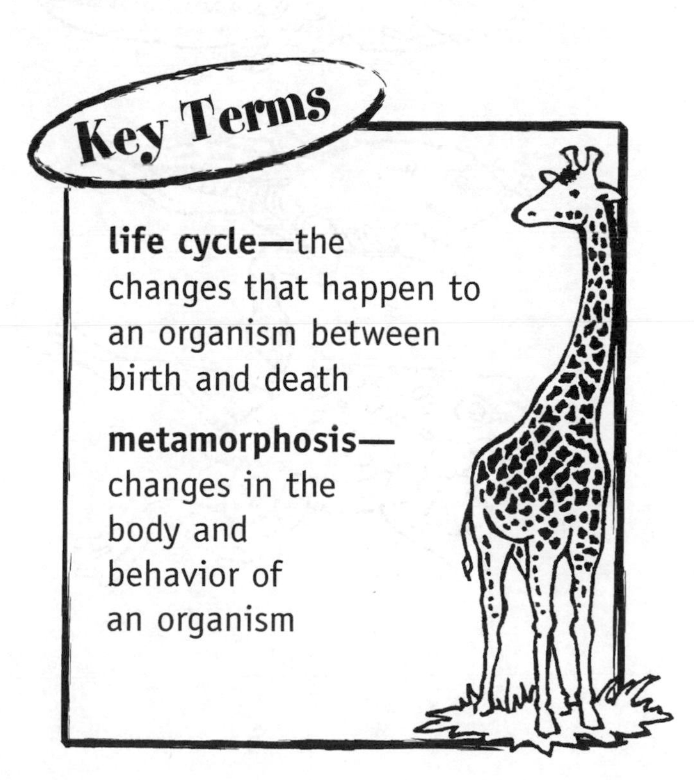

Key Terms

life cycle—the changes that happen to an organism between birth and death

metamorphosis—changes in the body and behavior of an organism

As tadpoles grow, they change. They form legs and lungs. These structures make them able to live on land. Their gills and tail disappear. They become adult frogs.

Adult frogs live mostly on land instead of in the water. Frogs usually stay near the water even when they are grown.

When frogs are ready to reproduce, they go back into the water. The female makes eggs, and the cycle begins again.

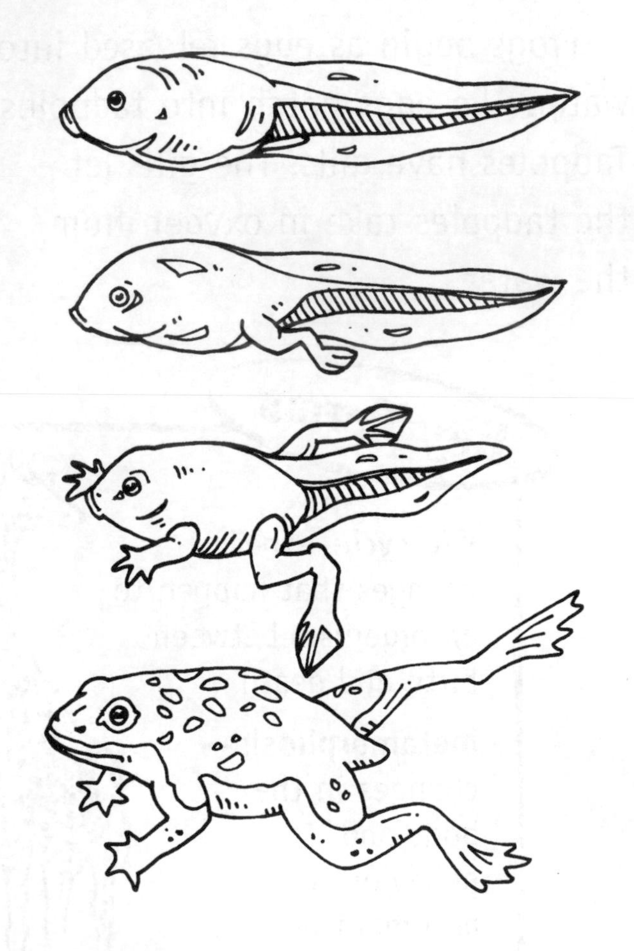

Insects also go through metamorphosis. In one type of insect metamorphosis, the young form looks like the adult form. Grasshoppers, dragonflies, and cockroaches go through this type of change. You can see this type of change in the picture below.

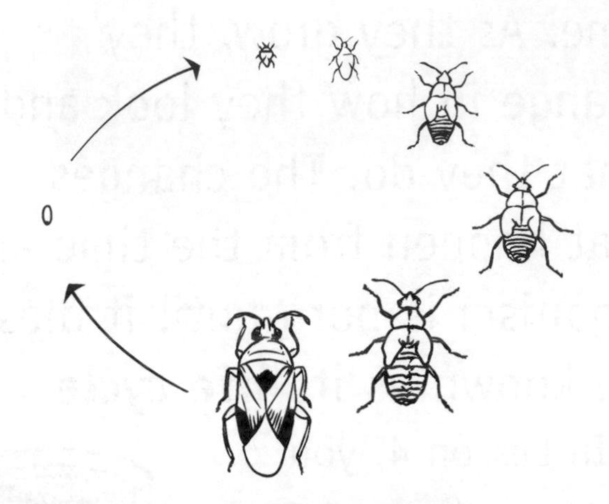

Butterflies, beetles, and bees go through a different type of metamorphosis. The young forms are very different from the adult forms. The picture below shows how a butterfly grows and changes from an egg.

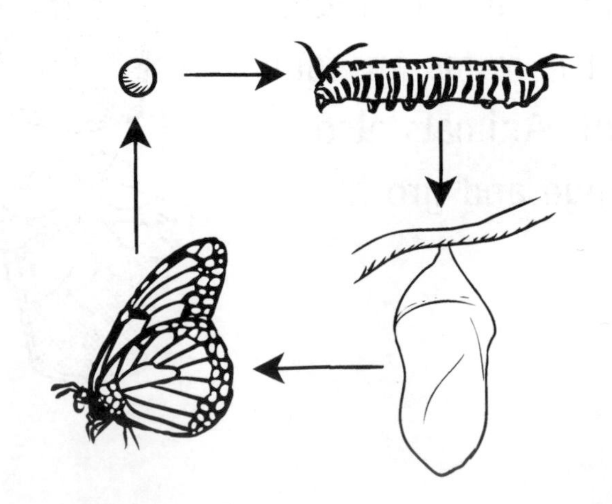

The Human Life Cycle

Humans also have a life cycle. Humans begin as one cell. The cell divides over and over again until it forms a baby. It takes nine months for a baby to form inside its mother. Then the baby is born.

A baby quickly grows in size. It also becomes able to do more things. Children grow and develop until they become adults. Even adults continue to change as long as they live.

NAME DATE

Lesson 5

Review

Darken the circle by the best answer.

1. Which best describes a life cycle?

Ⓐ how an organism looks when it is born

Ⓑ all the changes of an organism as it grows

Ⓒ how long an organism lives

Ⓓ the size of an organism

2. What is the first stage in the life cycle of many plants with flowers?

Ⓐ root

Ⓑ egg

Ⓒ flower

Ⓓ seed

3. Which organism goes through metamorphosis?

Ⓐ pine tree

Ⓑ elephant

Ⓒ frog

Ⓓ human

4. What does a tadpole use to breathe?

Ⓐ gills

Ⓑ lungs

Ⓒ tail

Ⓓ leaves

5. What is the first stage in the life cycle of an insect?

Ⓐ tadpole

Ⓑ egg

Ⓒ seed

Ⓓ spore

6. In their life cycle, humans begin as

Ⓐ a seed.

Ⓑ one cell.

Ⓒ many cells.

Ⓓ a baby.

NAME DATE

Review (cont'd.)

7. How are the types of insect metamorphosis different from one another?

8. A cycle happens over and over again. How does the life cycle of a plant or animal happen again?

NAME DATE

Lesson 5

Growing Up

Use magazines, newspapers, and other sources to find at least four pictures of young and adult animals. In the spaces below, make a poster showing the animals with their young.

Present your poster to the class. Describe how the young animal is different from the adult. Think about how the needs of the young might be different from the needs of the adult.

1	2
3	**4**

NAME DATE

Lesson 5

A Butterfly

The pictures show some of the stages in the life of a butterfly. They are out of order. Number the pictures from 1 to 4 to put them in the correct order.

NAME DATE

Lesson 5 The Emperor Penguin

Read the following passage. Then answer the questions that follow the passage.

In the cold temperatures of the Antarctic lives the largest penguin in the world. It is the emperor penguin. These penguins can be up to three feet tall. They can weigh as much as 100 pounds.

Although they are birds, emperor penguins do not fly. They can swim very fast in the ocean. They can slide on their bellies on the cold snow and ice. These penguins can also walk standing on two feet.

Emperor penguins have an unusual life cycle. When it is time to reproduce, these penguins walk away from the ocean. They can go as far as 60 miles inland. The mother penguin lays only one egg. She then gives the egg to the father. The father keeps the egg on top of his feet. The father has a flap of skin that holds the egg in place.

While the baby penguin grows inside the egg, the father does not move. Several fathers stand together to protect themselves from the cold winds. The fathers don't even eat food. All they eat is a little snow.

Once in a while, the father turns the egg over. This is to make sure the egg does not freeze. After about four months, the penguin chick hatches. The father makes a food that the penguin chick can eat.

After the chick hatches, the mother comes back. The father moves the chick from his feet to her feet. The father then goes to find food. After the chicks are older, the penguins go back to the ocean until it is time to have baby penguins again.

NAME DATE

The Emperor Penguin (cont'd.)

1. Where do emperor penguins live?

Ⓐ in the ice and snow of the Antarctic

Ⓑ in the warm and dry desert

Ⓒ in the wet and warm rain forest

Ⓓ in warm tropical oceans

2. Which is one way that emperor penguins do NOT move?

Ⓐ They walk on their feet.

Ⓑ They fly in the air.

Ⓒ They swim in the water.

Ⓓ They slide on their bellies.

3. What is the first stage in the life cycle of an emperor penguin?

Ⓐ chick

Ⓑ worm

Ⓒ fish

Ⓓ egg

4. What role does a father play in the life cycle of a young penguin?

Ⓐ He gathers food while the mother holds the egg.

Ⓑ He lays the egg and then gives it to the mother.

Ⓒ He protects the egg as the baby penguin grows inside it.

Ⓓ He carries the egg to the ocean and lets it go.

NAME DATE

Lesson 5

Experiment: Investigating the Life Cycle of a Frog

Frogs don't start out looking like frogs. In this activity, you will discover the life cycle of a frog.

What You Will Need

aquarium
gravel
water
water plants
rock
tadpoles
dried fish food
(All of these items may be included in a tadpole kit.)

Procedure

1. Place the aquarium in a place where it will not be disturbed. It should receive some light, but not direct sunlight.
2. Pour a thin layer of gravel on the bottom of the aquarium.
3. Add several inches of water. The aquarium should be a little less than half full.
4. Float some plants on the water. Push others into the gravel. Add a rock.
5. Put two or three tadpoles into the water.
6. Feed the tadpoles a small amount of dried fish food one time each day.
7. Add some fresh water to the aquarium once a week. Do not replace all of the water in the aquarium.
8. Observe the tadpoles every day. Make a table like the one shown. Write down how the tadpoles look and what they do. Every few days, make a drawing of what they look like.

NAME _______________ DATE _______________

Experiment: Investigating the Life Cycle of a Frog (cont'd.)

Analysis

Day	Observations

1. What changes did you see in the tadpoles?

____

____

____

2. How did they look after several weeks?

____

____

____

Conclusion

Describe the life cycle of a frog.

____

____

____

Lesson 6 Organisms and Environments

If someone asked you to find a bird's home, where would you look? You would probably look up in a tree. Many birds make their homes in trees.

Where would you look for a whale? You would probably look in the ocean. Whales need ocean water to live.

Organisms live where they can get what they need. Remember that living things need water, air, and food. The place where an organism gets what it needs is its environment. An **environment** is everything around a living thing. An environment includes other living things and nonliving things, too.

The picture shows a clownfish in its environment. There it gets everything it needs to live.

environment—everything around a living thing

ecosystem—the living and nonliving things in an environment

population—all of the same kind of organisms living in one area

community—all of the populations of organisms living in the same place

habitat—a part of an ecosystem where a population can get the things it needs

forest—an area in which the main kinds of plants are trees

desert—an ecosystem that gets very little rain

grassland—an ecosystem made up of large, flat areas of land covered with grass

fresh water—water that does not have a lot of salt in it

salt water—water that has a lot of salt in it

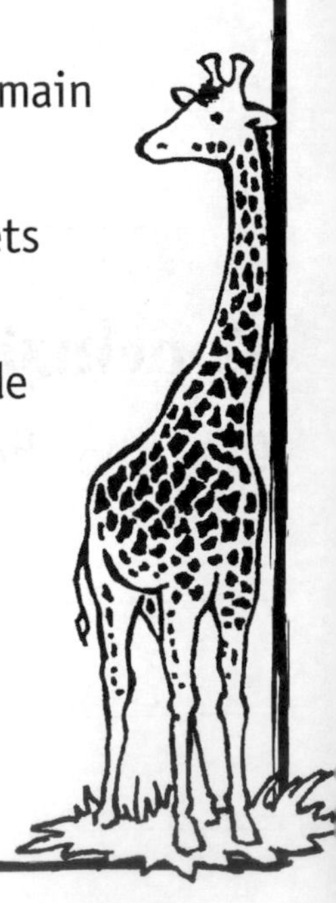

Parts of an Ecosystem

The living and nonliving things in an environment affect each other. Together, they form an **ecosystem**. There are many different kinds of ecosystems. Some are large and have many parts. An entire desert can be an ecosystem. Other ecosystems are smaller and have just a few parts. A simple fishbowl can be an ecosystem.

In each case, an ecosystem can be described by its parts. As an example, consider the ecosystem of the Florida Everglades. This ecosystem is made up of swampland covered by water and grasses. Many organisms live in the ecosystem.

A group of the same kind of living things that live in the same place at the same time make up a **population**. All of the short-tailed hawks in the ecosystem make up a population. Bobcats, alligators, and turkey vultures make up other populations in the same ecosystem. Even the mosquitoes make up a population.

Plants also make up populations. Red mangrove trees and bald cypress trees are important plant populations of this ecosystem.

All of the populations that live in the same area make up a **community**. The animals and plants of the Everglades form a community.

The organisms of a community affect each other in different ways. Remember that plants make oxygen that animals need. They also make food that animals use for energy. Animals often use plants for shelter.

Plants need animals because animals give off carbon dioxide when they breathe. Plants use this when they make food. Animals also help plants by carrying their seeds to places where they can grow.

Each population within the ecosystem might live in a different **habitat**. There can be many different habitats in the same ecosystem. The picture on page 68 shows some of the habitats of the Everglades. Some are in water. Fish and water plants live there. Some are on land. Pine trees and bobcats might live there.

Forest Ecosystems

All of the world's ecosystems can be placed into a few large groups. One such group is made up of forest ecosystems. A **forest** is an area in which the main kinds of plants are trees. There are several different kinds of forests. They are located in different places and have different kinds of plants and animals in them.

Deciduous Forests A deciduous forest is made up mostly of trees that lose their leaves in the fall. Maple and oak trees live in this type of forest. These forests are found in places that have warm summers and cold winters. They get enough rain for the trees to live throughout the year.

At the end of the summer, the temperatures become cooler and there is less rain. This causes the tree leaves to turn bright colors of orange, yellow, and red. Then the leaves fall to the ground.

Without leaves, the trees need less water and other materials. This helps them live through the cold winter. In the spring, the trees grow new leaves.

In addition to trees, ferns, mosses, and shrubs live in a deciduous forest. Animals include deer, bears, rabbits, squirrels, birds, and many insects.

Tropical Rain Forests A tropical rain forest is hot and wet all year long. The trees grow tall and stay green. The plants form layers. The top layer is called the canopy. It is formed by the branches and leaves of the tallest trees.

The next layer is the understory. It is formed by shorter plants and trees. At the bottom is the forest floor.

Different kinds of animals live in each layer. There are more types of plants and animals in a rain forest than in any other kind of ecosystem.

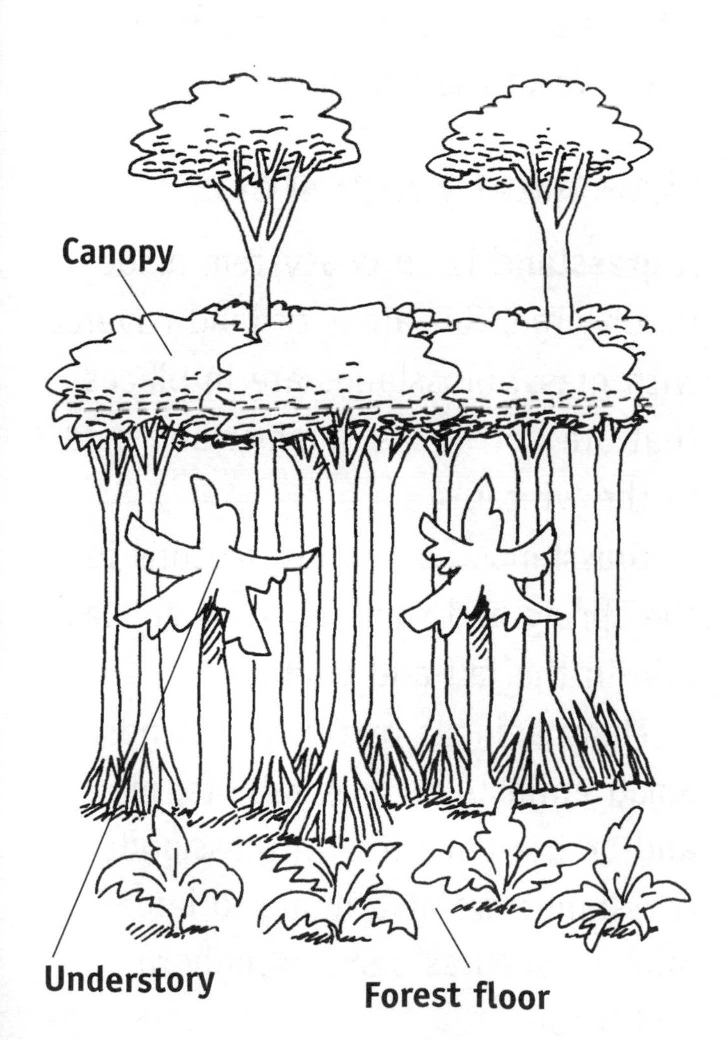

Coastal Forests A coastal forest grows where there is a lot of rain. These forests do not grow in very warm places like a tropical rain forest. They also do not grow where it is too cold.

They have thick trees and layers like in a tropical rain forest. Many animals, such as the northern spotted owl, live in coastal forests.

Coniferous Forests A coniferous forest is made up mostly of trees that have needle-like leaves. Pines, spruces, and firs live in these forests. These types of trees, known as conifers, are often called evergreens because they stay green all year.

Coniferous forests grow in places that have cool summers and very cold winters. They get less rain than other types of forests. The needle-shaped leaves help the trees save water. Moose, wolves, and bears are common in these forests.

Desert Ecosystems

A **desert** is an ecosystem that gets very little rain. Plants that grow in deserts must be able to live without a lot of water. The roots of most desert plants do not grow deep into the ground. They grow near the surface so they can soak up water whenever it rains.

Many desert plants have thick stems. The thick stems can save water for when the plant needs it. Some plants have spiny leaves. Their shape keeps the plant from losing water.

Animals that live in a desert get much of their water by eating plants. When they eat plants, they get the water stored in the plants.

Snakes and lizards in the desert stay in the shade during the hot days to keep cool. When the nights get cool, snakes and lizards stay warm by lying on rocks that were heated during the day.

Small mammals sleep in shelters during the hot days. Some burrow into the soil. At night, when it is cooler, they become active. Bats and rabbits are some of the mammals that live in the desert.

Grassland Ecosystems

A **grassland** is an ecosystem made up of large, flat areas of land covered with grass. Grasslands are in places that are hot in the summer and cold in the winter.

Grasslands have rainy seasons in the spring and summer. They get less rain in the fall and winter.

Many animals live in grasslands. Small animals such as rabbits, mice, and prairie dogs live in grasslands. Grasslands are also home to larger animals such as deer, pronghorn, and bison.

Freshwater Ecosystems

Lakes, streams, rivers, and ponds are freshwater ecosystems. **Fresh water** is water that does not have a lot of salt in it. The water in a river or stream is moving. The water in a lake or pond does not move.

Freshwater ecosystems have many plants and animals. The plants and animals live in and around the water. Different types of organisms live there, depending on how fast the water moves and how deep the water is.

Saltwater Ecosystems

Oceans and seas are saltwater ecosystems. **Salt water** is water that has a lot of salt in it. Some marshes and lakes also have salt water.

The amount of salt in saltwater ecosystems can be very different. It can even be different in places in the same ecosystem. Water near the surface is often less salty because rainwater adds fresh water to it. Along the shores, fresh water from streams and rivers may flow into the ecosystem.

Oceans are the largest ecosystems on Earth. There are many different kinds of plants and animals in them.

The ocean is usually described by different zones. The zones receive different amounts of sunlight. This makes some zones warmer than others. Different organisms live in each zone.

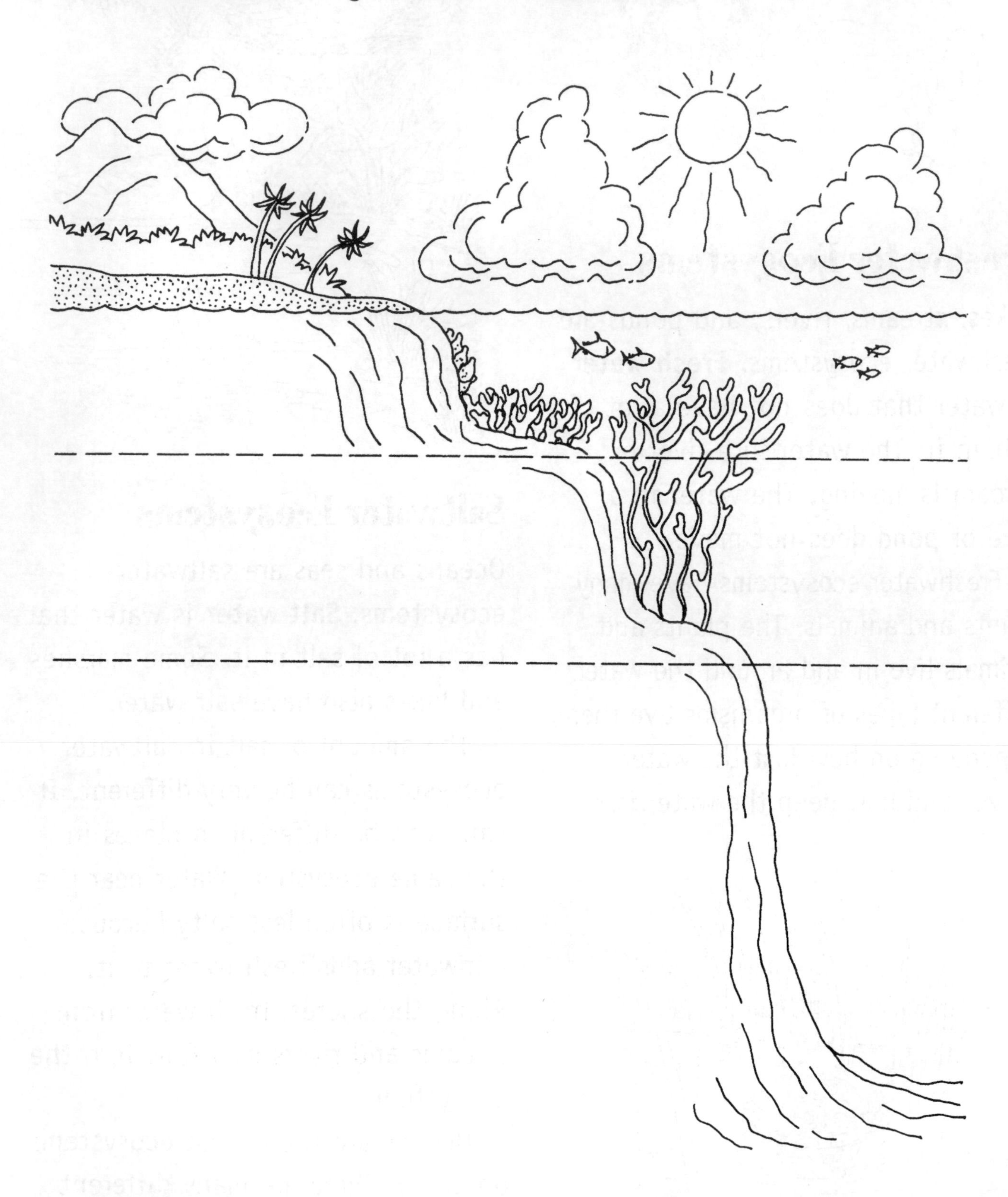

NAME DATE

Lesson 6

Review

Darken the circle by the best answer.

1. All of the same kind of living things in the same place at the same time make up

Ⓐ an ecosystem.

Ⓑ a population.

Ⓒ a community.

Ⓓ an environment.

2. Which is an example of a community?

Ⓐ all of the plants and animals in a pond

Ⓑ all of the alligators in a pond

Ⓒ all of the living and nonliving things in a pond

Ⓓ all of the water in a pond

3. Which type of ecosystem is an area in which the main kinds of plants are trees?

Ⓐ grassland

Ⓑ desert

Ⓒ forest

Ⓓ lake

4. Which is a major characteristic of the trees in a deciduous forest?

Ⓐ They have needle-like leaves.

Ⓑ They stay green all year round.

Ⓒ They lose their leaves in the fall.

Ⓓ They have thick stems that store water.

5. What are two kinds of water ecosystems?

Ⓐ warm and cold

Ⓑ freshwater and saltwater

Ⓒ shallow and deep

Ⓓ ones with plants and ones with animals

NAME DATE

Review (cont'd.)

6. How is a coastal forest different from a tropical rain forest?

7. What are two reasons why the amount of salt in a saltwater ecosystem might be different in different places?

NAME DATE

Lesson 6

Forest Ecosystems

Some forests grow in layers. The picture shows a rain forest. Write the names of the layers of the forest. Use the words in the box.

understory	forest floor	canopy

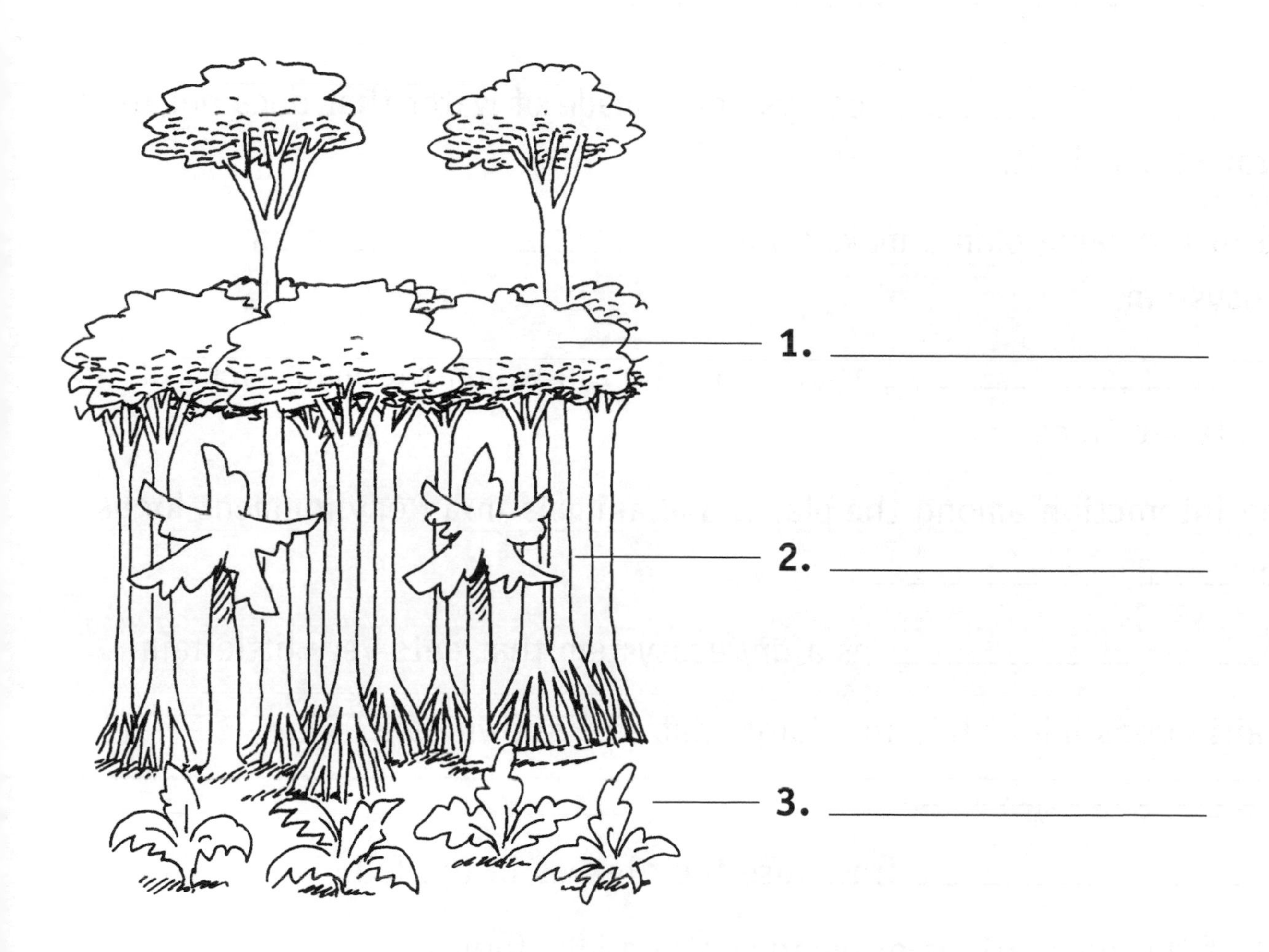

NAME ______________________ DATE ______________________

Lesson 6

All About Environments

On the lines, write the term that completes each sentence. Choose words from the word box below.

community	deciduous	forest	grassland	population
desert	ecosystem	freshwater	habitat	saltwater

1. A ______________________ ecosystem is made of water that does not have a lot of salt in it.
2. All of the same plants make up a ______________________ in an ecosystem.
3. A ______________________ is an ecosystem in which the main kinds of plants are trees.
4. The interaction among the plants and animals in an environment forms an ______________________.
5. A ______________________ is a dry ecosystem that gets very little rain.
6. Prairie dogs might live in a large, flat area known as a ______________________.
7. ______________________ trees lose their leaves in the fall.
8. All of the populations of organisms in a lake form a ______________________.
9. An ocean is a ______________________ ecosystem.
10. A bird's ______________________ is the part of its ecosystem where it can get the things it needs to live.

NAME DATE

Lesson 6 Organisms and Where They Live

Unscramble each of the clue words. These are words from the lesson. Take the letters that appear in ◯ boxes and unscramble them for the final word.

1. SEOTYECMS ◯ ☐ ☐ ☐ ☐ ☐ ☐ ☐ ◯
2. SERTOF ☐ ☐ ◯ ☐ ☐ ☐
3. DEERST ☐ ☐ ☐ ☐ ☐ ◯
4. CUMOIMYTN ☐ ☐ ☐ ☐ ☐ ◯ ☐ ☐ ☐
5. LOTNUPIPAO ☐ ◯ ☐ ☐ ☐ ☐ ☐ ☐ ☐ ◯
6. TABTIAH ☐ ☐ ☐ ◯ ☐ ☐ ☐
7. DANLASRGS ☐ ☐ ☐ ☐ ☐ ☐ ☐ ◯ ☐
8. HEFSAERRTW ☐ ☐ ◯ ☐ ☐ ☐ ☐ ☐ ☐ ☐
9. ☐ ☐ V ☐ ☐ ☐ ☐ ☐ ☐ ☐ ☐

NAME DATE

Lesson 6 Losing Ecosystems

Read the following passage. Then answer the questions that follow.

Earth is covered by many different ecosystems. In parts of the world, ecosystems are being cut down. One such ecosystem is the tropical rain forest. Almost two acres of rain forest are cut down every second!

There are many reasons why rain forests are being cut down. One reason is to get wood. Rain forest trees make beautiful wood. People use that wood to make furniture, floors, and art.

Another reason rain forests are being cut down is to clear land for farms. The problem is that the soil in a rain forest is not good for farming. In a few years, farmers must cut down more trees to find new land to farm.

Losing rain forests affects everyone. When rain forests are cut down, the organisms that live there lose their homes. Many of them become extinct. This means that no more of these organisms live on Earth anymore. Some scientists think that over 100 types of rain forest plants, animals, and insects become extinct every day.

In addition, the plants in a rain forest help clean Earth's air. They also make fruits and nuts. Many rain forest organisms contain chemicals that can be used as medicines. When the trees are cut down, all of these things are lost.

1. What is happening to Earth's rain forests?

Ⓐ They are forming in new habitats.

Ⓑ They are growing larger.

Ⓒ They are being destroyed.

Ⓓ They are becoming cool and dry.

NAME DATE

Losing Ecosystems (cont'd.)

2. What is a reason why rain forests are being destroyed?

Ⓐ No animals live in them.

Ⓑ They are not getting enough rain.

Ⓒ People want to make farms.

Ⓓ There is not enough air for them.

3. What most likely happens to the birds in a tree when the tree is cut down?

Ⓐ The birds grow bigger because they have more space.

Ⓑ The birds do not survive because their habitat is gone.

Ⓒ The birds learn to live on the ground.

Ⓓ The birds find a way to regrow the tree.

NAME DATE

Lesson 6 Experiment: Investigating Environments

The conditions of an environment depend on where it is located. In this activity, you will find out where the major types of environments are located.

What You Will Need

blank world map
colored pencils
atlas or encyclopedia

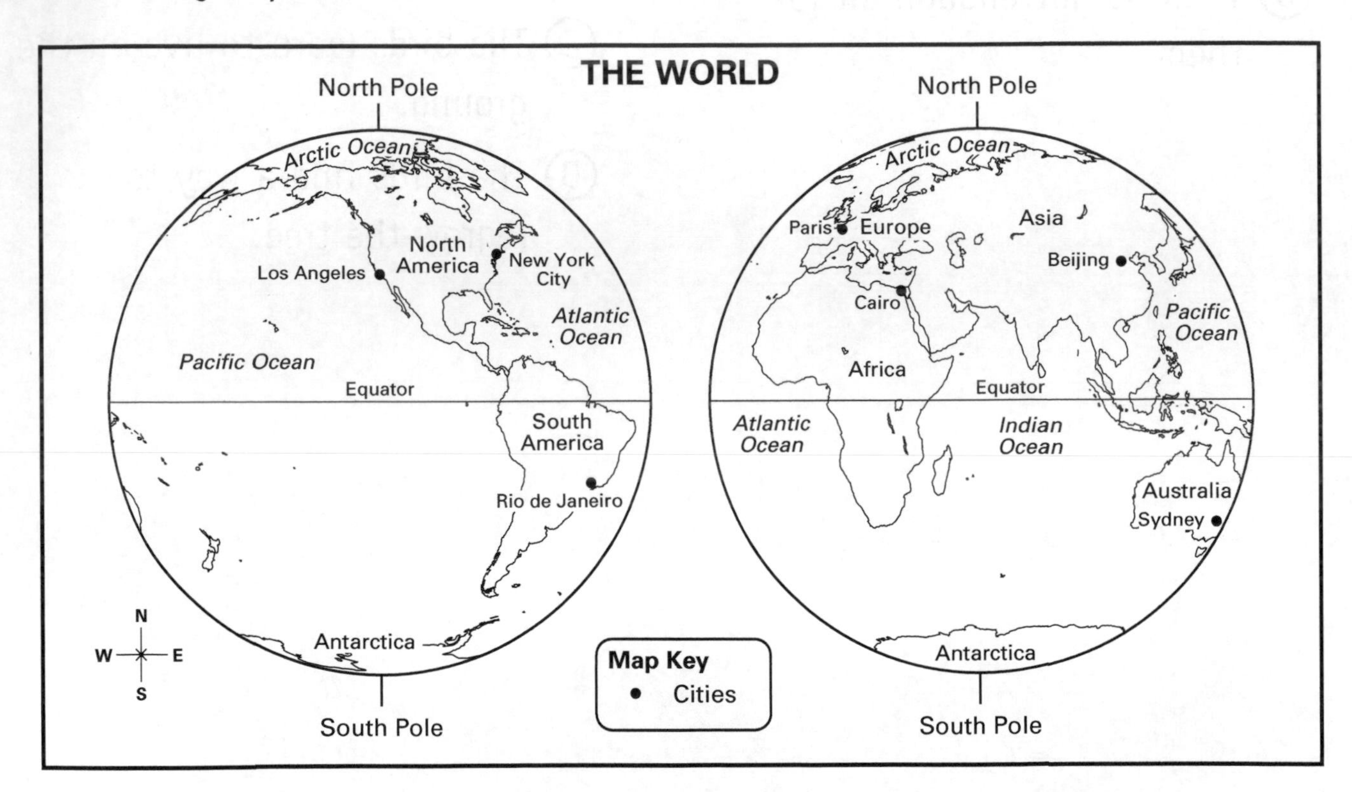

Procedure

1. Choose a color for each type of environment: tropical rain forest, coastal forest, grassland, desert, and ocean. For example, ocean will be blue. Desert might be brown. Make a key to describe your map.

NAME _______________ DATE _______________

Experiment: Investigating Environments (cont'd.)

2. In research books, find out where each type of environment is found. Color these places on the map according to your key.
3. The equator is an imaginary line around the center of Earth. Compare the location of each type of environment with the location of the equator.

Analysis

1. Which environments are closest to the equator?

____

____

____

2. Which type of environment covers most of Earth?

____

____

____

Conclusion

How does the distance to the equator affect an environment?

____

____

____

Lesson 7 Properties of Earth Materials

Look at a handful of shiny pennies. You are looking at a mineral called copper. A **mineral** is a solid object that was formed in nature and has never been alive.

There are many different kinds of minerals. Gold is a shiny mineral. Diamond is the hardest mineral. Chalk is a very soft mineral.

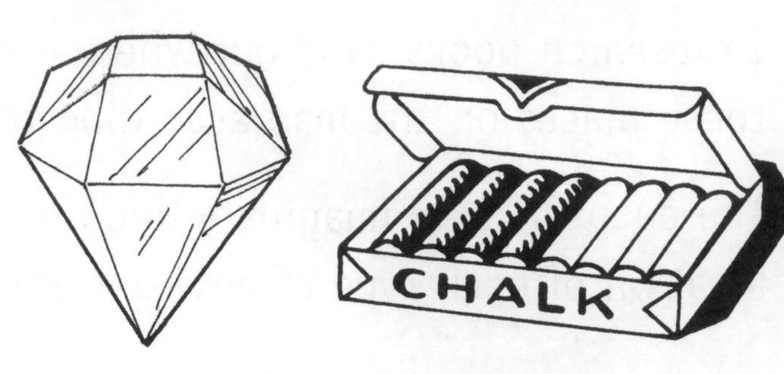

Using Minerals

Have you used a mineral today? You probably have and didn't even know it. The average person uses 40,000 pounds of minerals every year!

Key Terms

mineral—a solid object that was formed in nature and has never been alive

rock—a solid object made of minerals

sediment—bits of rock

sedimentary rock—rock that forms in layers from bits of rock

igneous rock—rock that forms when lava or magma cools

metamorphic rock—rock that forms through changes in other rocks

rock cycle—the process during which one type of rock changes into another type of rock

weathering—the process through which rock is broken into small pieces

erosion—the process through which natural forces, such as wind and water, carry away bits of rock and other materials over time

delta—an area of land that forms when sediment is dropped at the mouth of a river

soil—the loose material that plants need to grow

Did you write with a pencil today? The dark material in the pencil is the mineral graphite. The bed you slept in last night might have parts made of iron or nickel.

If you drank out of a glass or ate out of a bowl, you might have used more minerals. Glasses and bowls are often made of minerals such as silica, limestone, talc, and feldspar.

Did you use anything that has a battery? Many batteries are made from the minerals copper or lead.

Your body needs small amounts of some minerals to stay healthy. Iron and zinc are minerals in some of the foods you eat. So are phosphorus, potassium, and calcium.

Rocks

Earth is made up mostly of rocks. A **rock** is a solid object made of minerals. People use rocks in many ways. They use rocks to make roads. Rocks are also used to make statues and buildings.

Rocks are formed in three different ways. One way is when small bits of rock and other materials pile up in layers. The bits of rock are called **sediment.** As the layers get thicker, they squeeze together. Over time, the sediments change into solid rock. This type of rock is called **sedimentary rock.**

Sedimentary rock

Another way that rock forms is from hot lava. When lava from a volcano cools down, it forms solid rock. Sometimes lava forms under Earth's surface. It is called magma. Magma can also cool into rock. This type of rock is called **igneous rock.**

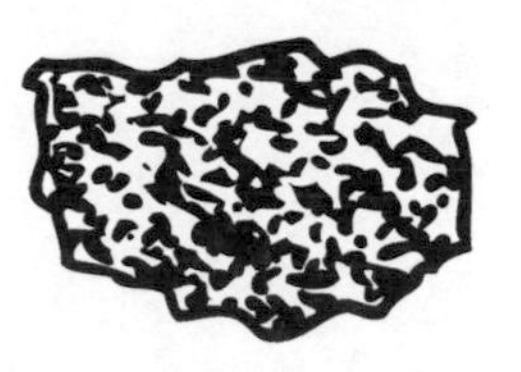

Igneous rock

Rocks under Earth's surface can become very hot. In addition, the rocks are pushed from all directions. This pushing is called pressure. The heat and pressure can change rocks into a different kind of rock. Rock formed in this way is called **metamorphic rock.**

Metamorphic rock

The Rock Cycle

Each type of rock can be changed into another type. The process of rocks changing into other types of rocks is called the **rock cycle**.

The diagram shows the rock cycle. If you follow the arrows, you can see how one rock changes into another.

Some changes happen because of high heat and pressure. Other changes happen when rocks break apart to form sediments.

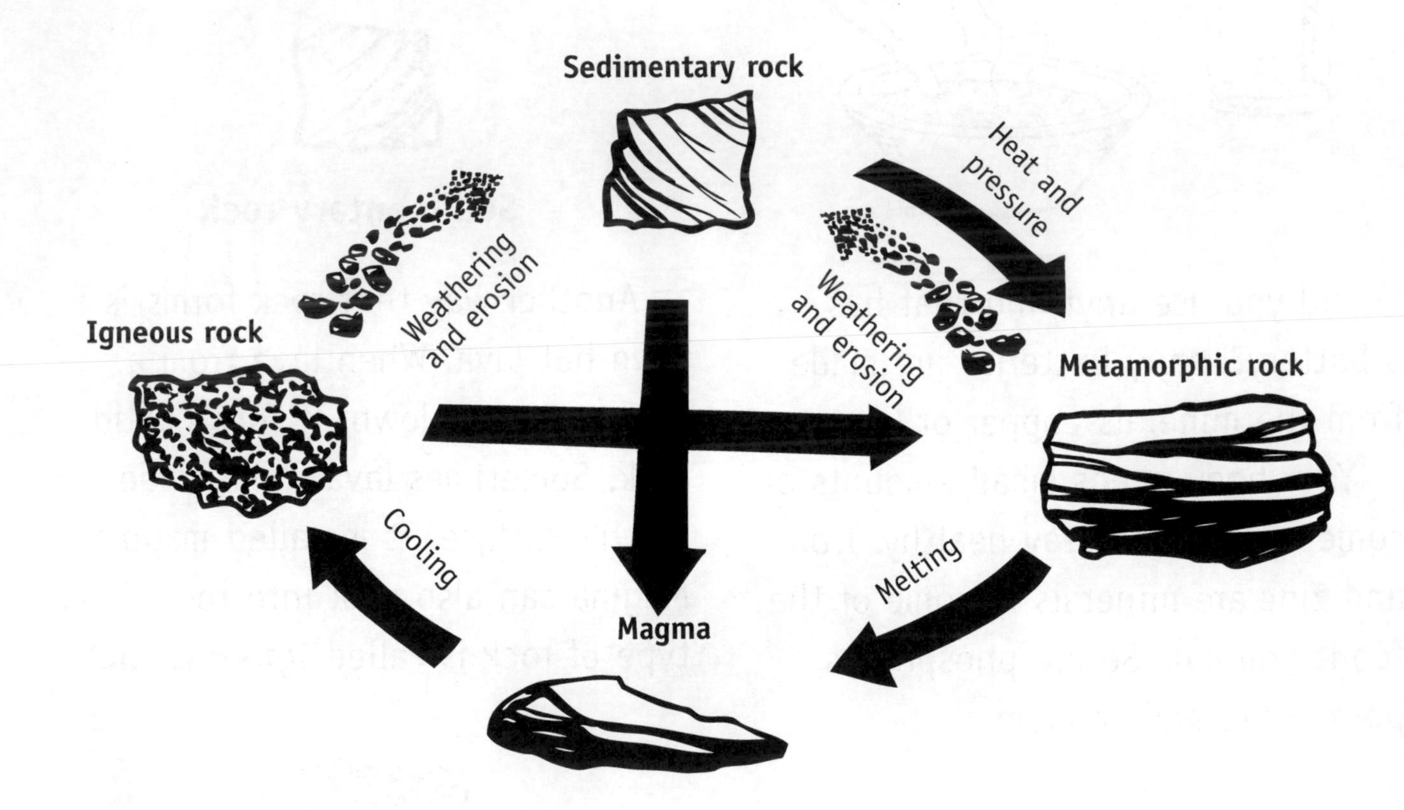

Weathering

You saw in the rock cycle that rocks can be broken apart. **Weathering** is the process through which rocks are broken into smaller pieces.

Weathering happens in several different ways. One way is by wind. When wind blows across a rock over many years, the rough edges of the rock are worn away. Water flowing over a rock can do the same thing.

Another way that water weathers rock is when it freezes. Water can flow into the cracks or spaces in rock. When it gets cold, the water freezes into ice. Ice is bigger than liquid water. The ice pushes the rock apart, breaking it into pieces.

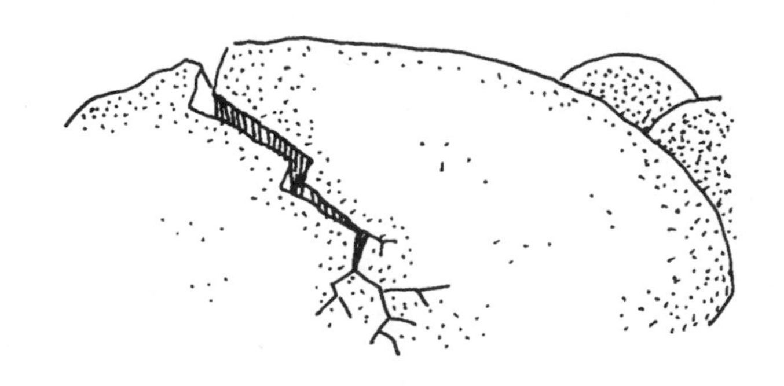

Living things can cause weathering, too. Plant roots can grow into cracks in rocks. As the roots get bigger, they split the rock into pieces.

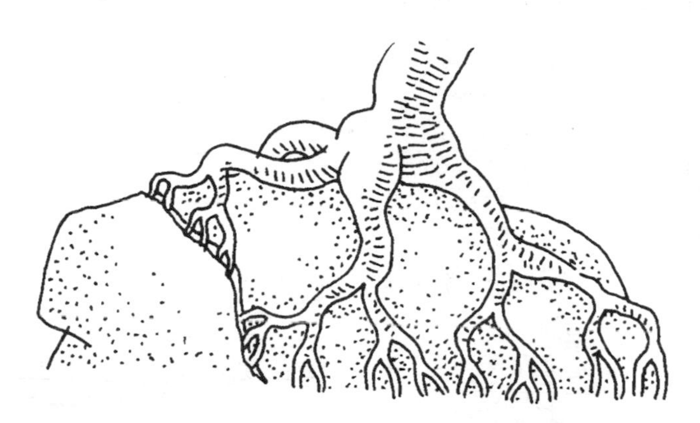

Erosion

What happens to the pieces that are broken off rocks during weathering? Many of them are carried away by erosion. **Erosion** is the movement of weathered rock and soil.

Just as wind and water can cause weathering, they can also cause erosion. Bits of rock can be carried by blowing winds or flowing water.

Once the wind or water slows down, the bits of rock are dropped in a new place. This is how deltas are formed. A **delta** is an area of land that forms at the mouth, or end, of a river. As the river slows down, bits of rock drop out of the water. Over time, these bits of rock pile up.

Soil

Weathering and erosion are important in making soil. **Soil** is the loose material that plants need to grow.

Weathered rock is a major part of soil. Soil also contains parts of organisms that were once alive. This part of soil is called humus. Decaying leaves make up a large part of humus.

Spaces form between the bits of rock in soil. Water and air fill some of these spaces.

Soil forms in layers as shown in the diagram. The process is not fast. It can take up to 1,000 years to form just 1 inch of soil.

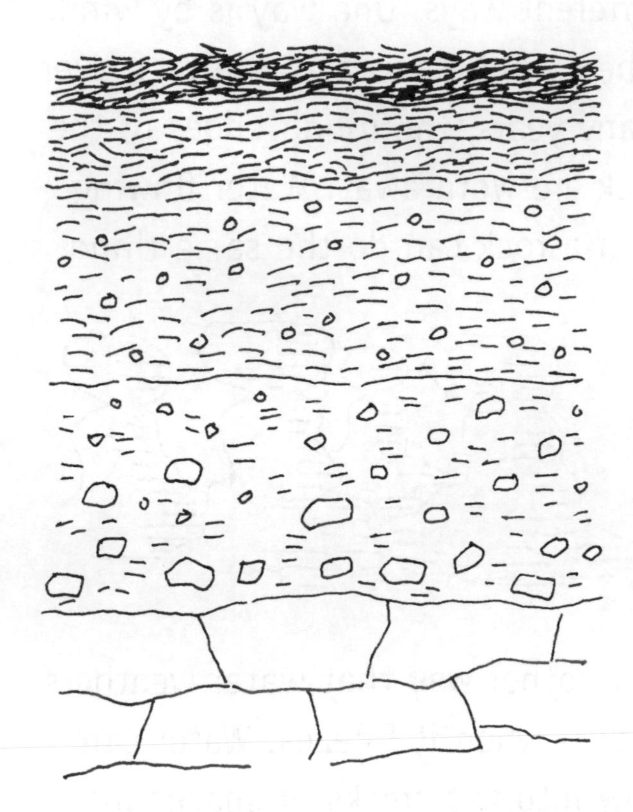

NAME ____________________ DATE ____________________

Lesson 7

Review

Darken the circle by the best answer.

1. Which of these is a property of all minerals?

- Ⓐ They were never alive.
- Ⓑ They must be shiny.
- Ⓒ They must be hard.
- Ⓓ They must cost a lot of money.

2. Which of the following is rock that forms in layers?

- Ⓐ metamorphic
- Ⓑ igneous
- Ⓒ lava
- Ⓓ sedimentary

3. What is the main process that happens during the rock cycle?

- Ⓐ Water in rock is frozen into ice.
- Ⓑ Sediment in water is dropped in a new place.
- Ⓒ One type of rock is changed into another.
- Ⓓ One mineral is changed into another.

4. What happens when rock is weathered?

- Ⓐ It is formed when two rocks combine.
- Ⓑ It is broken into small pieces.
- Ⓒ It is melted by heat.
- Ⓓ It grows larger over time.

5. What is humus in soil?

- Ⓐ sediment carried by erosion
- Ⓑ water that flows into spaces
- Ⓒ solid rock at the bottom
- Ⓓ remains of living things

6. What are three ways that people use minerals?

____

____

7. How is soil important to people?

____

____

NAME DATE

Lesson 7

Earth's Materials

Write a key term to complete each sentence. Choose from the words below.

cycle	erosion	metamorphic	sediment	soil
delta	igneous	rock	sedimentary	weathering

1. ________________ rock is formed when lava from a volcano cools.
2. Rock is broken into small pieces through the process of ________________.
3. Small bits of rock are known as ________________.
4. Weathered rock and once-living materials form ________________ that plants need to live.
5. Layers of broken rock and bits of living things form ________________ rock over time.
6. Under Earth's surface, heat and pressure change sedimentary or igneous rocks into ________________ rock.
7. A person might skip a ________________ into a lake or use it to make a road.
8. Weathered rock is moved to a new place through ________________.
9. The rock ________________ describes how one type of rock changes into another.
10. Bits of rock dropped at the mouth of a river form a ________________.

NAME ______________________ DATE ______________________

Lesson 7

Naming Earth's Materials

Each term below is missing at least one letter. Fill in the missing letters to complete the words. Choose from the letters in the box. Then use each term in a sentence.

A	I	L	N	P	S
G	K	M	O	R	

1. ERO___IO___

____

2. META___OR___HIC ROCK

____

3. M___NERA___

____

4. WE___THE___ING

____

5. I___NE___US ROCK

____

6. ROC___

____

Lesson 7

The Hawaiian Islands

Read the following passage. Then answer the questions that follow the passage.

The Hawaiian Islands are some of the most beautiful places in the world. The islands were formed by magma from under the sea. The source of this magma is known as the Hawaiian hotspot.

Earth's land is broken into pieces that can move slowly. These pieces are called plates. About 6 million years ago, the Hawaiian hotspot produced magma. As the magma cooled, it formed the island of Kauai.

Kauai had volcanoes. Magma from the hot spot came up through the volcanoes. Over time, the plate moved. Magma no longer came up through the volcanoes. So the volcanoes on Kauai died out.

The magma from the Hawaiian hotspot then formed another island. This island became known as Oahu. The plate moved again, and the volcanoes on Oahu died out.

The plate kept moving and formed the islands of Maui and Hawaii. The volcanoes on the youngest islands are still active. That means they still produce lava from time to time.

South of the island called Hawaii, another island is forming. The process is slow, though. There won't be another Hawaiian Island for about 10,000 years.

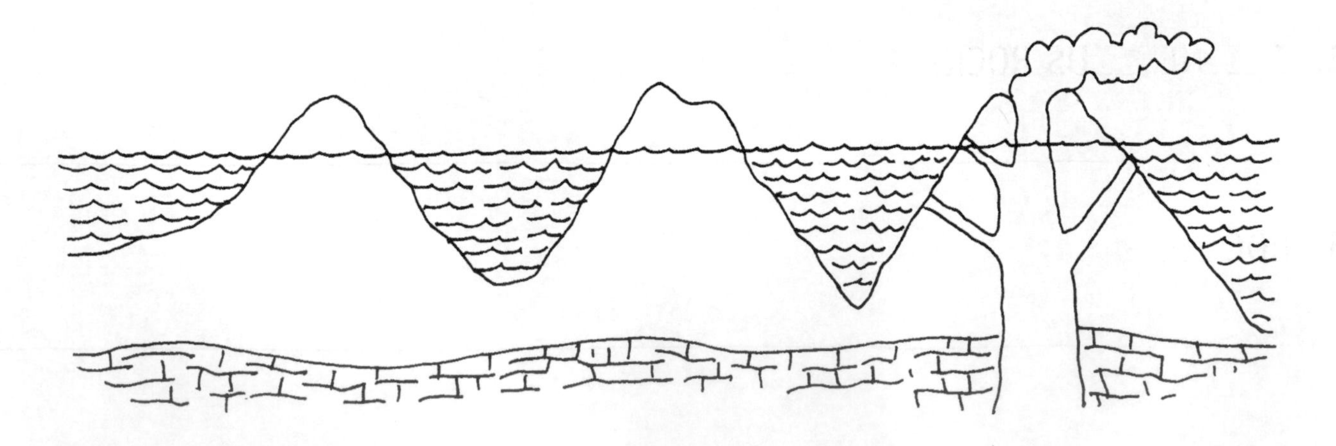

NAME DATE

The Hawaiian Islands (cont'd.)

1. How were the Hawaiian Islands formed?

Ⓐ Waves from the ocean wore away old rock.

Ⓑ Layers of broken rock washed up from the ocean.

Ⓒ Magma cooled into solid rock.

Ⓓ One of Earth's plates broke into pieces.

2. The plate under the Hawaiian Islands moves. What does this mean about the ages of the islands?

Ⓐ All the islands are the same age.

Ⓑ Kauai must be the oldest island.

Ⓒ Hawaii must be the oldest island.

Ⓓ There is no way to compare the ages of the islands.

3. What will happen to the volcanoes on the island of Hawaii as the plate keeps moving?

Ⓐ They will fall into the ocean.

Ⓑ They will form into more volcanoes.

Ⓒ They will get bigger.

Ⓓ They will die out.

4. According to the passage, what do scientists think will happen to the Hawaiian Islands in the future?

Ⓐ There will be another island.

Ⓑ At least one island will disappear.

Ⓒ The islands will join to form one big island.

Ⓓ The islands will be buried under water.

NAME DATE

Lesson 7 Experiment: Investigating Soil

There are many different kinds of soil. Some are very sandy. Others have lots of materials from living things in them. In this activity, you will find out how the type of soil affects how water moves through it.

What You Will Need

2 paper cups
pencil
sand
potting soil
3 liquid measuring cups
water

Procedure

1. Using the pencil, carefully poke 10 small holes in the bottom of each paper cup.
2. Fill one cup half full of potting soil. Fill the other cup with the same amount of sand.
3. Place each cup in a measuring cup.
4. Slowly pour one cup of water into the cup of potting soil. Then repeat for the cup of sand.
5. Pick up each paper cup and hold it over its measuring cup for about two minutes.
6. Set the paper cups aside on a paper towel. Measure how much water is in each measuring cup. Write down your measurements.

NAME ____________________ DATE ____________________

Experiment: Investigating Soil (cont'd.)

Analysis

Soil	Amount of water
Potting soil	
Sand	

1. Why did you need to use the same amount of soil in each paper cup?

2. Which soil particles are larger—those in potting soil or in sand?

3. Which measuring cup had the most water in it?

Conclusion

Which soil allowed more water to pass through it? How is this related to the sizes of the particles in the soil?

Lesson 8 Objects in the Sky

Have you ever heard anyone say that you are on the "third rock from the sun"? In a way, that is just what Earth is. Earth is a planet. A **planet** is a large body of rock or gas that moves around the sun. The path an object takes as it moves around another object in space is called an **orbit.**

Earth is not the only planet. There are eight planets altogether. There are some other objects that orbit the sun, too. The sun and the objects that orbit it make up the **solar system.**

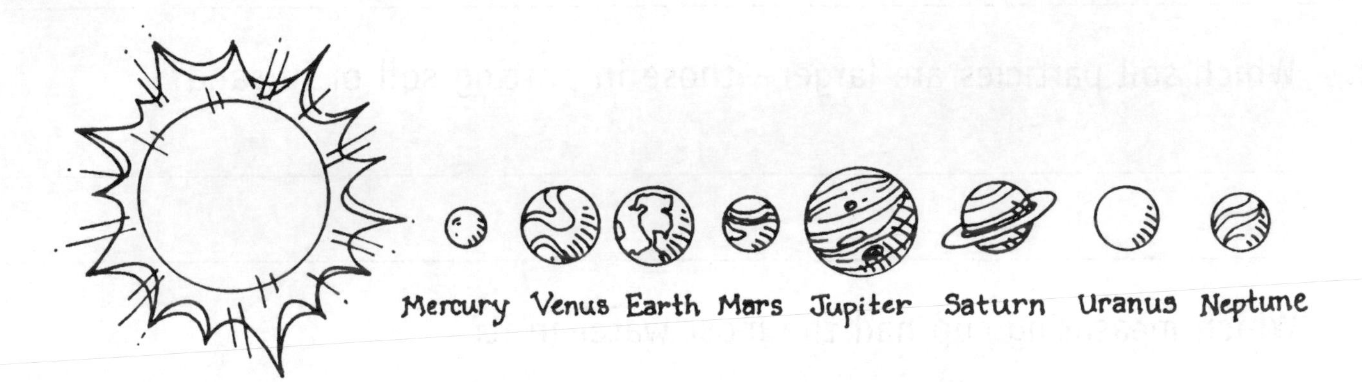

Key Terms

planet—a large body of rock or gas that moves around a star

orbit—the path an object follows as it travels around another object in space

solar system—the sun and the objects that orbit it

star—a ball of glowing gases

asteroid—a small, rocky object that orbits the sun

comet—a small amount of ice and dust that orbits the sun in a long path

meteor—a piece of dust or rock that glows as it enters Earth's atmosphere

The Sun

The sun is at the center of the solar system. The sun is a star. A **star** is a ball of glowing gases.

The sun is huge compared to the planets. All of the planets of the solar system could fit inside the sun.

When compared with other stars, the sun is average in size. Many stars are larger. Some are smaller. The sun looks bigger than other stars in the sky because it is closer to Earth than any other star.

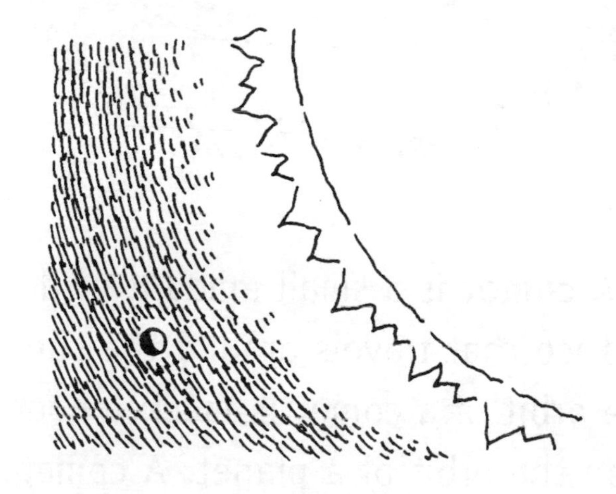

The Planets

The four planets closest to the sun are called the inner planets. They are Mercury, Venus, Earth, and Mars. The inner planets have rocky surfaces.

Some planets have moons. A **moon** is a rocky object that orbits a planet. Earth has one moon. Mars has two moons.

Earth is different from the other planets because it has liquid water on its surface. It also has a lot of oxygen in its atmosphere. These conditions make it possible for plants and animals to live on Earth.

Mercury

The four planets that are farthest from the sun are called the outer planets. They are Jupiter, Saturn, Uranus, and Neptune.

Most of the outer planets are bigger than the inner planets. Jupiter is the largest planet in the solar system.

The outer planets are colder than the inner planets because they are farther away from the sun. The outer planets are made mostly of frozen gases. Most of the outer planets have many moons. Some have rings around them made of dust and ice.

Pluto was once called a planet. In 2006, scientists decided that Pluto is not a true planet like the others.

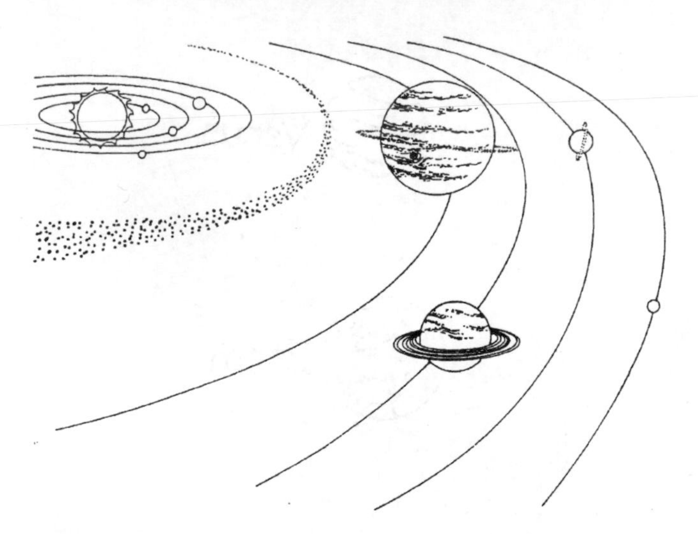

Asteroids, Comets, and Meteors

Along with the planets, some other objects are parts of the solar system. These include asteroids, comets, and meteors.

An **asteroid** is a chunk of rock that orbits the sun. Asteroids can be anywhere in the solar system. Most of them are located in a belt between Mars and Jupiter.

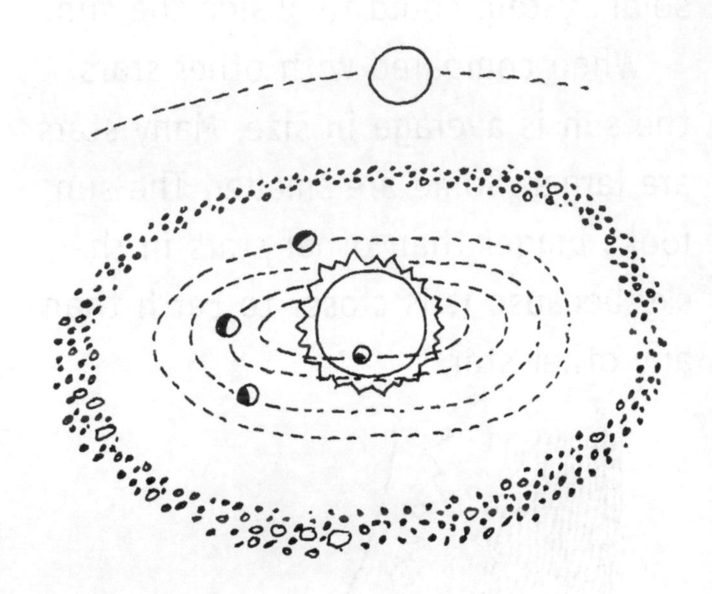

A **comet** is a small amount of dust and ice that travels around the sun. The orbit of a comet is much longer than the orbit of a planet. A comet can come close to the sun and then move past Neptune.

People can see comets only when they pass close to the sun. When this happens, some of the ice in the comet melts into a long, glowing tail. The tail can be very long. This is what can be seen from Earth.

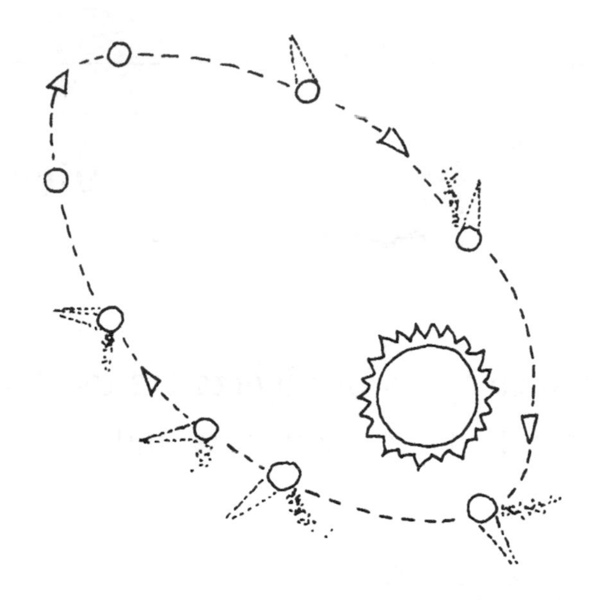

This shows a comet's orbit around the sun. When a comet gets close to the sun, the comet can develop one or two tails.

A **meteor** is a piece of dust or rock that glows as it enters Earth's atmosphere. People sometimes call meteors shooting stars. Most of a meteor burns up as it travels through Earth's atmosphere. There are usually a few meteors every night. Hundreds of meteors that can be seen on the same night make up a meteor shower. Meteors that don't burn up and hit Earth's surface are called meteorites.

NAME DATE

Lesson 8

Review

Darken the circle by the best answer.

1. Which of these is NOT a planet?

Ⓐ Earth
Ⓑ Jupiter
Ⓒ Saturn
Ⓓ the sun

2. Why does the sun look larger than any other star in the sky?

Ⓐ It is the largest star there is.
Ⓑ It is closer to Earth than any other star.
Ⓒ It is filled with planets.
Ⓓ It is the only star that glows.

3. How is Earth different from all of the other inner planets?

Ⓐ It orbits the sun.
Ⓑ It is made of rock.
Ⓒ It has liquid water on it.
Ⓓ It has a moon.

4. Which types of objects are located in a belt between Mars and Jupiter?

Ⓐ asteroids
Ⓑ planets
Ⓒ stars
Ⓓ comets

5. At what part of its orbit can people on Earth see a comet?

Ⓐ when it passes Neptune
Ⓑ when it comes close to the sun
Ⓒ when it falls to Earth
Ⓓ when it blows up

NAME DATE

Review (cont'd.)

6. What are three ways that the outer planets are different from the inner planets?

Made of frozen gases
colder ma
many Moons

7. How is the orbit of a comet different from the orbit of an asteroid?

a comet has a long pathe

NAME DATE

Lesson 8

The Solar System

The diagram shows the solar system. Use the words below to label the parts of the solar system.

planet	sun	asteroids	moon

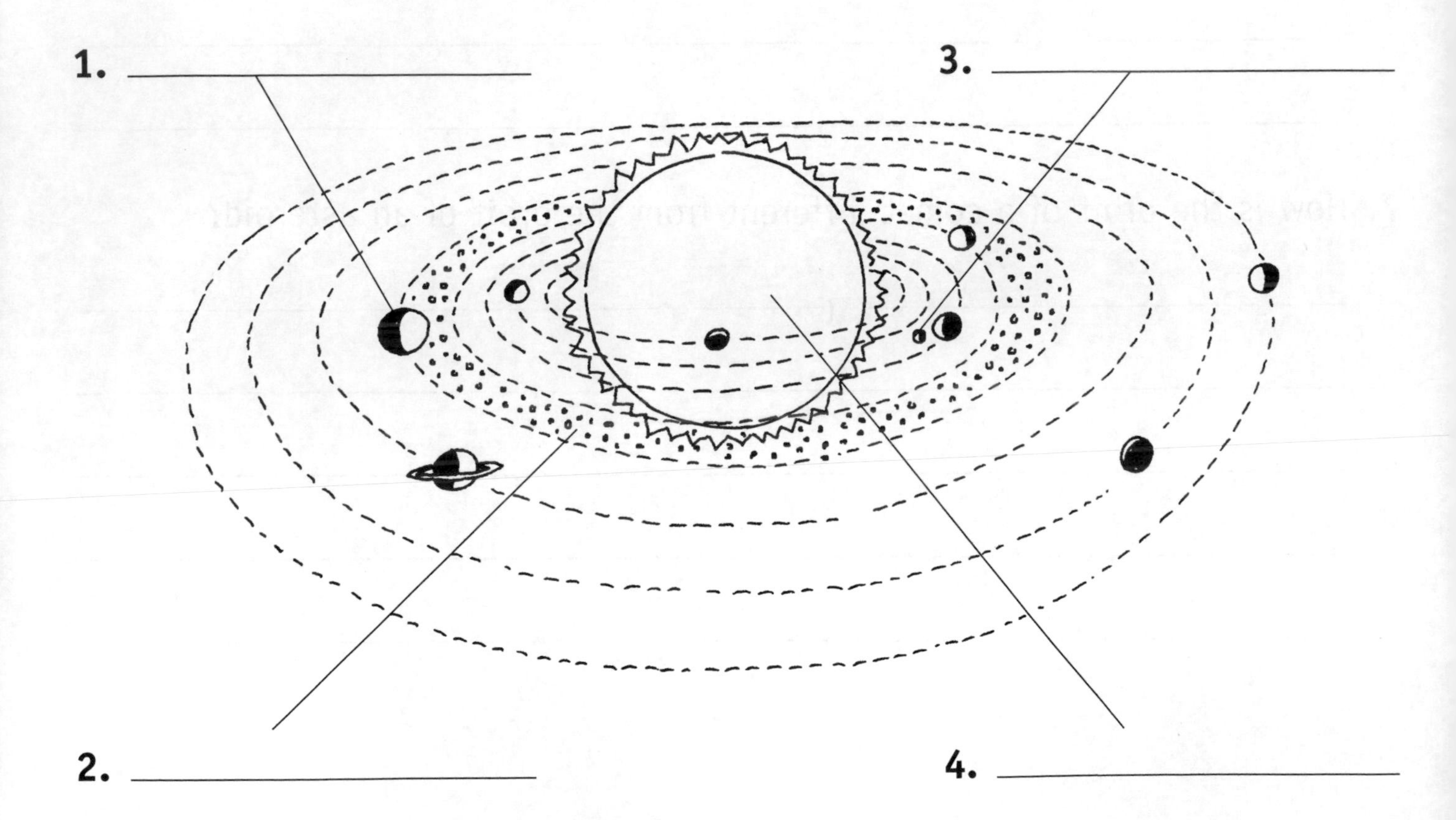

NAME ______________________ DATE ______________________

Lesson 8

Finding Objects in the Sky

Circle the following words in the puzzle below. They may appear horizontally, vertically, or diagonally. Then underline the first 30 letters not circled. Write the letters on the lines below the puzzle to spell out a secret message.

ASTEROID	EARTH	ORBIT	RINGS	STAR
COMET	MOON	PLANET	SOLAR	SUN

```
T H E R E A R E A M T A Z I N
G O B D I O R E T S A I J E C
P L A N E T S T M S I N B T H
E S K Y X G J J S O L A R R Z
Q S Z S N Z J H G G O C O B O
C W Q I A A Z B U D S N O I M
B V R A B Q K Q P E U U H U C
R A T S P Y X P M G H U K K D
K G Y T J S H F O J S E H U C
H T R A E J V Z N E G D H Z E
Q J B C D K E N U H N N T C S
F B G H O M R O S F J C C O U
O R D L V M P J C F P J K S A
L M U F S C E W L Y A N O S O
Q K V J Z G Y T O Z K D T B M
```

_ _

_ _ _ _ _ _ _ _ _ _ _.

NAME DATE

Lesson 8 A New Way to Think About the Solar System

Read the following passage. Then answer the questions that follow the passage.

You know that the sun is in the center of the solar system. For a long time, people did not know this. Two thousand years ago, people thought that Earth was in the center of the solar system. They believed that the sun moved around Earth.

You may wonder why they thought this. The main reason has to do with the sun. If you watch the sun during the day, it looks as if it moves across the sky. People figured that the sun must move around Earth.

In 1543 a man named Nicholas Copernicus described a different idea. He suggested that the sun just looks as if it is moving. He said that a person on Earth might think that the sun is moving even though it is not.

The idea had been mentioned before, but it was never believed. The way that Copernicus explained the idea made people slowly change how they looked at the solar system.

1. What did people think was true about the solar system 2,000 years ago?

(A) Earth was the only planet.

(B) The sun was the only star.

(C) The sun moved around Earth.

2. Why does the sun look as if it moves across the sky?

(A) It rises in one direction and sets in another.

(B) It gets bigger in the morning and smaller at night.

(C) It moves in circles in the sky.

3. What did Copernicus believe about the solar system?

(A) Earth moves around the sun.

(B) The sun moves around Earth.

(C) Earth moves around the moon.

NAME DATE

Lesson 8 Experiment: Investigating Models

Scientists use models to study the solar system. In this activity, you will build your own model.

What You Will Need

paper
tape
markers
ruler
scissors

Procedure

1. Cut out a large paper circle to represent the sun. You can color it yellow if you wish.
2. Tape the sun on a wall.
3. Cut eight smaller circles out of paper. Write the name of a planet on each circle.
4. Use tape to attach the planets to the wall. Place them at the distances listed in the table. For example, place Mercury 6 centimeters away from the sun. Place Venus 10 centimeters away from the sun. Continue until you have taped all of the planets on the wall.

Planet	Mercury	Venus	Earth	Mars	Jupiter	Saturn	Uranus	Neptune
Distance	6 cm	10 cm	14 cm	22 cm	74 cm	136 cm	280 cm	428 cm

NAME DATE

Experiment: Investigating Models (cont'd.)

Analysis

Were all of the planets the same distance from the sun? Explain.

Conclusion

How do models of the solar system help scientists study it?

Unit 3 Earth and Space Science

Lesson 9 Changes in Earth and Sky

What's your favorite season of the year? Some people enjoy cold winters. Others like warm summers. Whatever you choose, the seasons are caused by the movements of Earth.

Earth moves in two ways. One way is by spinning on an imaginary line called an **axis**. The axis goes from the North Pole to the South Pole. The spinning of an object on an axis is called **rotation**. Earth's rotation on its axis is one day. One day lasts 24 hours.

The second way that Earth moves is in an orbit around the sun. The movement of one object around another is called **revolution**. Earth's revolution around the sun is one year. One year lasts a little more than 365 days.

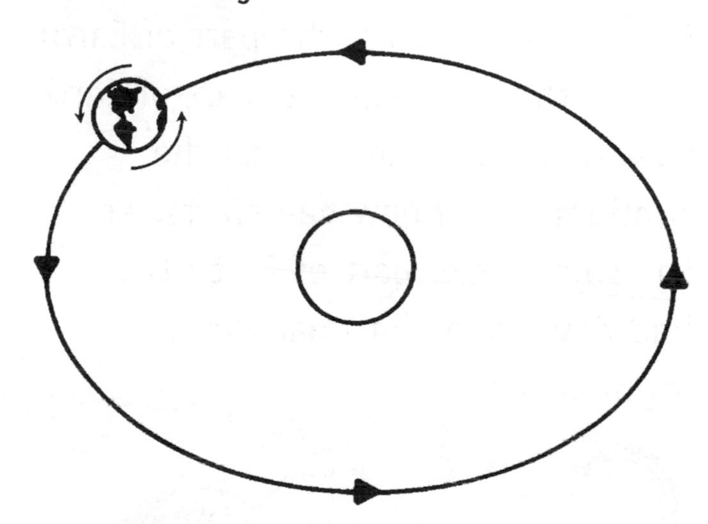

Key Terms

axis—an imaginary line that runs from the North Pole to the South Pole of Earth

rotation—the spinning on an axis

revolution—the movement of one object around another

crater—a dent in the surface of the moon

phases—the changes in how the moon looks because of its motion around Earth

lunar eclipse—when the moon moves into Earth's shadow

solar eclipse—when Earth moves into the moon's shadow

Day and Night

When it is lunchtime in California, it might be time to go to bed in Italy. While some places on Earth have day, other places have night.

Day and night are caused by Earth's rotation. At any time, half of Earth faces the sun. The side of Earth facing the sun is lit and has day. The other half is in darkness and has night.

As Earth rotates, the part of Earth facing the sun changes. Part of Earth that had night moves into the sunlight and a new day starts. At the same time, part of Earth that had day moves into darkness. Night begins.

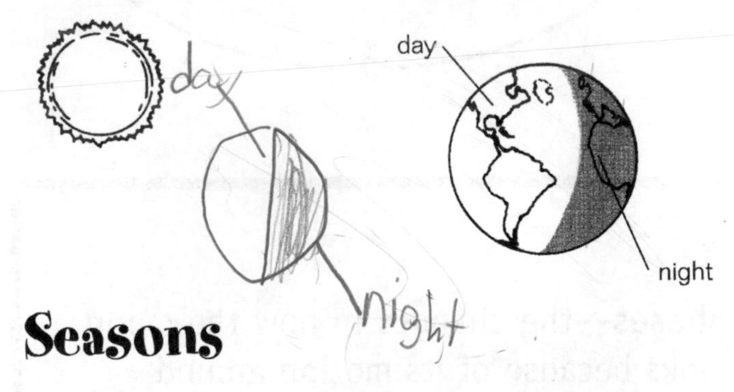

Seasons

Earth's axis is tilted. It always tilts the same way. Remember that Earth moves around the sun. This means that for part of the year, the top of the axis (the North Pole) points toward the sun.

When Earth is in this position, sunlight is almost straight when it hits the northern half of Earth. This makes the northern half of Earth get more light and heat. Days are longer and warmer. The northern half of Earth has summer.

At the same time, the bottom of the axis (the South Pole) points away from the sun. Sunlight does not hit the southern half of Earth straight on. Days are shorter and cooler. The southern half of Earth has winter.

Three months later, Earth has moved into a new position. Neither part of the axis points toward the sun. The length of day and night is equal. Temperatures are cooler than summer, but warmer than winter. It is fall in the northern half of Earth. It is spring in the southern half.

In another three months, Earth has moved to another position. Now the northern half points away from the sun and has winter. The southern half points toward the sun and has summer.

In three more months, neither part of Earth points toward the sun again. This time, the northern half has spring. The southern half has fall. As Earth moves, the cycle starts again.

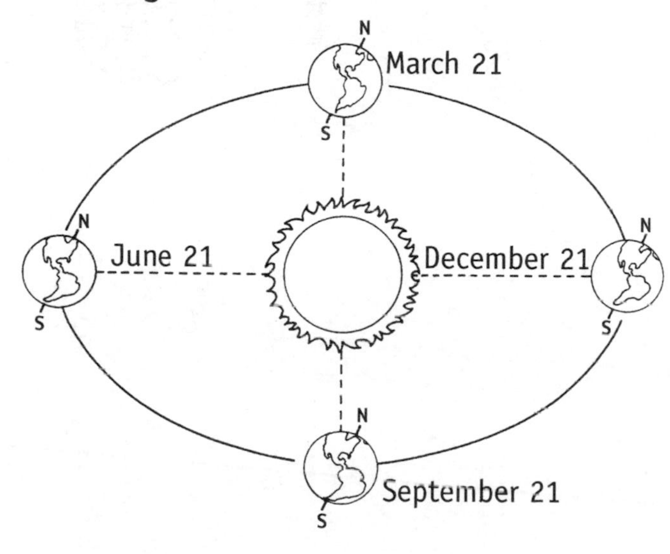

The Moon

The moon orbits Earth. The moon is a large rock. It has dents in it called **craters**. A crater is formed when a rocky object crashes into the moon.

Like Earth, the moon rotates on its axis. It also revolves around Earth. The moon rotates in about the same amount of time as it revolves. The moon rotates and revolves in about 29 Earth days.

If you look at the moon on some nights, it looks like a big ball. On other nights, the moon looks like a thin line. It even seems to disappear on some nights.

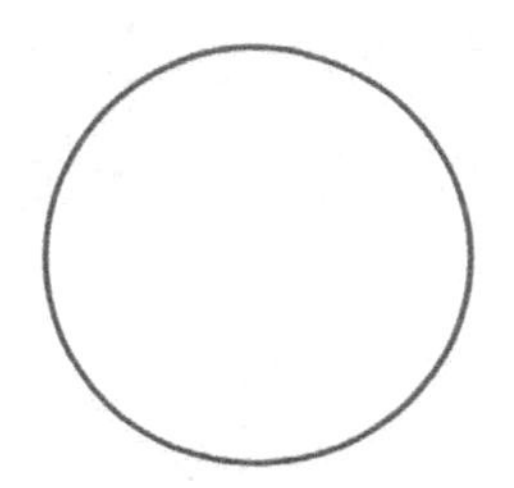

The moon does not actually change at all. Only the way you see it changes. Like Earth, half of the moon is always lit by the sun. As the moon orbits Earth, you can see different parts of the lit half of the moon.

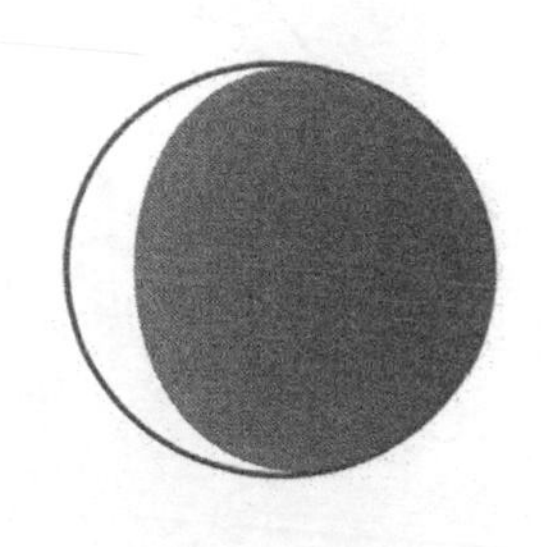

The different shapes that the moon seems to have are called **phases**. The moon goes through all its phases every $29\frac{1}{2}$ days. The phases are shown in the picture.

Eclipses

If you stand out in the sun, you can make a shadow. A shadow forms when some sunlight is blocked.

Everything in the sun can make a shadow. Trees, houses, and mailboxes make shadows, too.

Sometimes Earth gets between the moon and the sun. Earth blocks some of the light from the sun and makes a shadow. As the moon orbits Earth, it passes into that shadow. This is called a **lunar eclipse**.

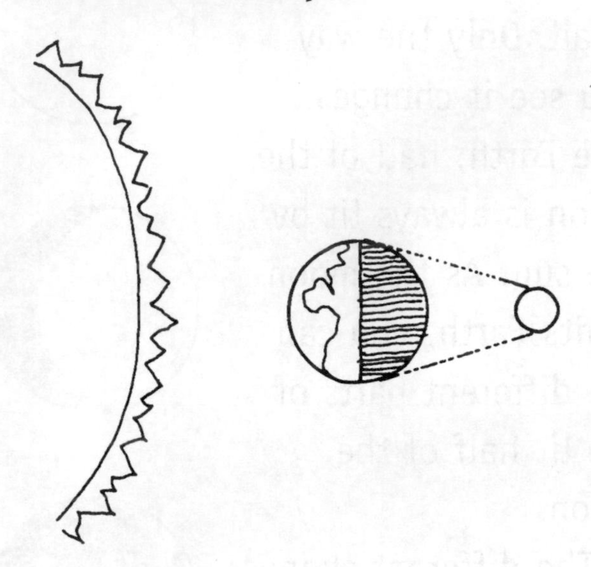

The moon sometimes moves between Earth and the sun. This time, the moon blocks some of the sun and makes a shadow. A **solar eclipse** happens when the moon's shadow falls on Earth.

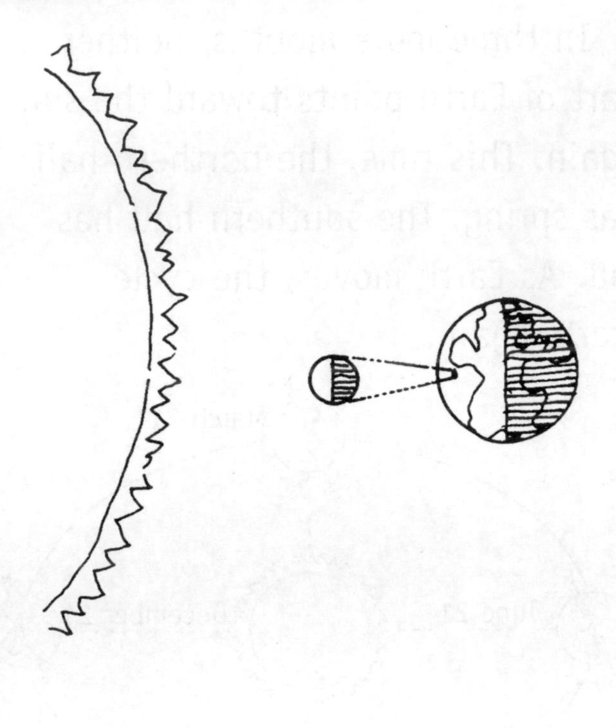

NAME ______________________ DATE ______________________

Lesson 9

Review

Darken the circle by the best answer.

1. How long does it take for Earth to rotate on its axis?

Ⓐ 1 minute

Ⓑ 1 hour

Ⓒ 1 day

Ⓓ 1 year

2. How does Earth move when it revolves?

Ⓐ It spins on its axis.

Ⓑ It orbits the sun.

Ⓒ It tilts from one side to the other.

Ⓓ It changes shape.

3. What change is caused by Earth's tilt?

Ⓐ seasons

Ⓑ day and night

Ⓒ years

Ⓓ eclipses

4. What season does the southern half of Earth have when it points toward the sun?

Ⓐ spring

Ⓑ fall

Ⓒ winter

Ⓓ summer

5. Why can you see phases of the moon?

Ⓐ You can see different parts of the lit half of the moon.

Ⓑ The moon changes in shape during the month.

Ⓒ The moon gets bigger and smaller.

Ⓓ You see different moons during the month.

NAME ____________________ DATE ____________________

Review (cont'd.)

6. Why wouldn't there be seasons if Earth's axis did not tilt?

____

____

____

____

____

7. How is a solar eclipse different from a lunar eclipse?

____

____

____

____

____

NAME DATE

Lesson 9 Changes in the Sky

Fill in the puzzle with the terms described by each clue. Choose from the word box below.

axis	moon	revolution
crater	orbit	rotation

Across

3. The huge rock that orbits Earth
4. A dent on the moon caused by a rock crashing into it
5. The name of Earth's path around the sun

Down

1. Earth's motion around the sun
2. Earth's spinning motion

NAME DATE

Lesson 9 Seasons

The diagram below shows Earth as it revolves around the sun. The numbers on the diagrams point to four different places on Earth. For each number, write WINTER if the place is having winter and SUMMER if the place is having summer.

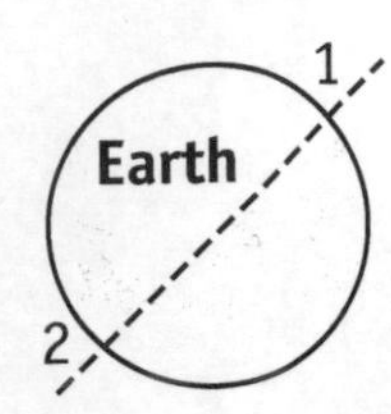

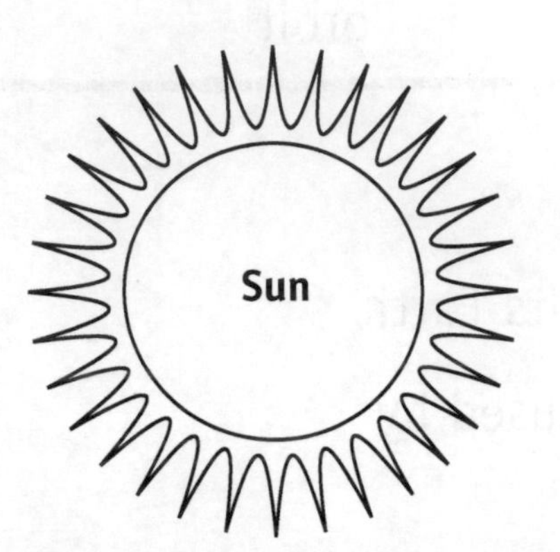

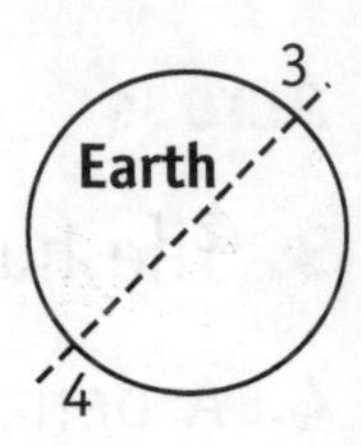

1. ______________________________

2. ______________________________

3. ______________________________

4. ______________________________

NAME DATE

Lesson 9

Calendars

Read the following passage. Then answer the questions that follow the passage.

You can keep track of the days of the year using a calendar. The type of calendar that you might hang on your wall is a type of solar calendar. The word *solar* describes something that relates to the sun. A solar calendar is based on Earth's position in its revolution around the sun.

The calendar has 365 days separated into 12 months. It actually takes Earth a little bit longer than 365 days to orbit the sun. If the calendar did not do something about this, there would be 6 extra hours every year. This may not sound like a lot, but after 100 years there would be an extra 24 days. The seasons would not match the calendar.

To prevent this problem, an extra day is added to the calendar every 4 years. This is known as a leap year. The day is added to the end of February. In most years, February has 28 days. In leap years, February has 29 days.

Not everyone uses a solar calendar. Some people use a lunar calendar. The word *lunar* describes something that relates to the moon. This type of calendar relates to the phases of the moon.

The Islamic calendar is a lunar calendar. It has 12 months that are 29 or 30 days each. This results in a year that has either 354 or 355 days. The months of the year in this calendar do not match up with the seasons of the year.

There are some calendars that combine parts of solar and lunar calendars. The Chinese calendar is this type of calendar.

Calendars (cont'd.)

1. Based on the word *solar*, what is the source of solar power?

   Ⓐ water

   Ⓑ Earth

   Ⓒ the moon

   Ⓓ the sun

2. How many months are in a solar calendar?

   Ⓐ 4

   Ⓑ 6

   Ⓒ 12

   Ⓓ 24

3. What happens during a leap year?

   Ⓐ There are only 10 months.

   Ⓑ There is an extra day.

   Ⓒ There is an extra month.

   Ⓓ There are no seasons.

4. What is a lunar calendar based on?

   Ⓐ the phases of the moon

   Ⓑ the seasons of the year

   Ⓒ the number of people using it

   Ⓓ the rotation of the planet

NAME ______________________________ DATE ______________

Lesson 9 Experiment: Investigating Seasons

Seasons are described by different temperatures and periods of sunlight. In this activity, you will find out how Earth's motion causes seasons.

What You Will Need

globe
light bulb (lamp without a shade)
masking tape

Procedure

1. Find where you live on the globe. Place a piece of tape there.
2. Hold the globe so that the axis is tilted.
3. Place the lamp on a desk or table so that it shines on the globe.
4. Dim the other lights in the room. Move the globe around the light bulb.
5. Stop at four different places around the light. Look at how the light hits the tape in each place.

Analysis

Where did the globe point when light hit your town straight on?

____

Conclusion

Why are there seasons where you live?

____

____

Science Fair Project Guide

You can use a science fair project to learn about the world. A science fair project is like the activities you do in science class.

You follow many of the same steps. A science fair project takes a bit longer. It involves more time and observations.

Choose a Topic

The first thing you need to do is find a topic you like. Do you like animals or plants? Do you want to study rocks? Maybe you like space and weather. Choose what you will study. This is your topic.

The next step is to ask a question about your topic. If you like rocks, you might ask,

"How is one rock different from another?"

If you like weather, you might ask,

"Can you predict the weather from the clouds you see?"

Gather Information

The next thing to do is to learn about your topic. You can use books, magazines, and the Internet.

You can also talk to people who know about the topic. You might ask a person at a local news station about weather. You might ask a person at a nearby garden center about plants.

Types of Projects

There are three basic types of projects.

An Experiment An experiment is made up of steps you follow to answer your question. This type of project involves choosing a variable. The *variable* is something that you will change.

For example, suppose you grow two plants. They are the same in every way except for one. You add plant food to the soil of one plant. You do not add it to the other. Plant food is the thing you change. It is your variable.

You use your variable to state a hypothesis. A *hypothesis* is your guess about what you think will happen.

Your hypothesis might be that a plant that gets food will grow better. You don't know that this is true. You guess that it will be true. You will find out if you are right as you do your project.

To test your hypothesis, you design and conduct an experiment. You should make observations during the experiment. An *observation* is something you learn using your senses.

You might make notes about how each plant looks. You might measure the height of each plant over time. You might make drawings of the plants. You might even take photographs of them on different days. Any information you get is known as your *data*.

When you are finished, you *analyze your results*. This means that you think about your data. You try to figure out what it means. For example, you need to figure out if the plant with food grew better than the other plant.

You *draw a conclusion* by deciding what happened. You might conclude that the plant with food did grow better than the other plant.

You must also decide if your conclusion supports your hypothesis. In this case, it does. You thought that the plant food would help a plant grow better, and it did.

Your project is not a failure if your conclusion does not support your hypothesis. Your goal was to answer a question.

Even if your conclusion tells you that the hypothesis was not true, you still learn something about your topic. The goal of science is to learn about the natural world.

An Exhibit Not all science projects involve experiments. Some science projects are used to teach other people about a topic.

This type of project can be a model, display, or demonstration. It should include an essay that describes the exhibit. It should have pictures that relate to the exhibit. You can use this type of project to show a process. For example, you might show what happens when a volcano erupts.

A Collection This type of project involves classifying objects. To *classify* means to place objects into groups by how they are alike and different.

For this type of project, you might collect a number of objects. The objects should be items from the natural world such as rocks or leaves. They should not be objects that people make, such as stamps, coins, or toys.

You then study the objects and decide how to classify them. For example, you might group rocks by their color or sparkle. You might group leaves by their shape and size.

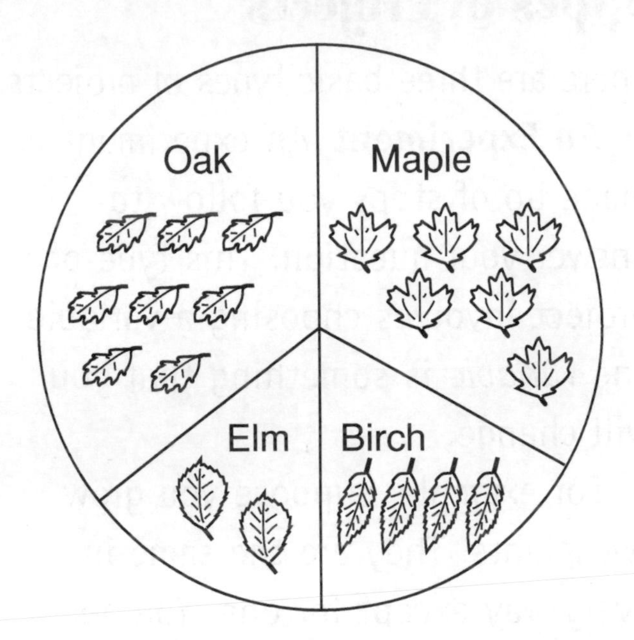

Safety

The most important part of any science project is to stay safe. Always listen to your teacher or parent.

Check with your teacher or parent before starting a project. Check with your teacher or parent if you are not sure something is safe. Let your teacher or parent know right away if you have an accident.

Always wear safety goggles. These will keep your eyes safe from chemicals. They will also keep your eyes safe from any things that come loose.

Tell your teacher or parent right away if any chemicals do touch your eyes or skin. Flush your eyes or skin with running water for several minutes.

Tie back long hair. Don't wear loose clothing. Never taste, touch, or smell anything unless your teacher or parent tells you to.

Do not eat or drink around your project. Things from your project can get into your food. Your food might also ruin your project.

Project Notebook

Write down notes about your project. Keep your notes in a notebook.

You should have the following pages.

Title Page This page should list the title of your project. It should also have your name, your teacher's name, and the date.

Table of Contents This page should list what is in your report. It should give the page number of each part of the report.

Overview This page should tell why you did the project. It should tell what you did and what you learned.

Materials This page should give a list of all the materials that you used. It should tell the sizes of items or how many you used.

Experiment and Data Write all of the steps that you followed. Show drawings or photos of steps when you can.

Write notes about what you observed. Show graphs and charts of what you found.

Conclusion This page tells what you discovered. It should tell if your results supported your hypothesis.

Sources Anything you used to learn about your topic is called a source. List all the sources you used. Tell the name of the source. Also tell who wrote or published the source and when.

List all the people you spoke with. Give their titles and where they work.

Presenting the Project

Scientists share their results. In the same way, you should share what you learned.

Show your science notebook. Make a display. The display should be neat and easy to follow.

Your display should tell about your project. It should show any pictures, graphs, or charts you made. It should also show any objects you collected.

Project Ideas

There are many great ideas for science fair projects. Here are some questions you might think about.

You might use one of these. Or, they might give you an idea for something different.

- **Does matter keep the same shape and volume in different containers?** Compare how the shape and volume of solids, liquids, and gases change in different containers.

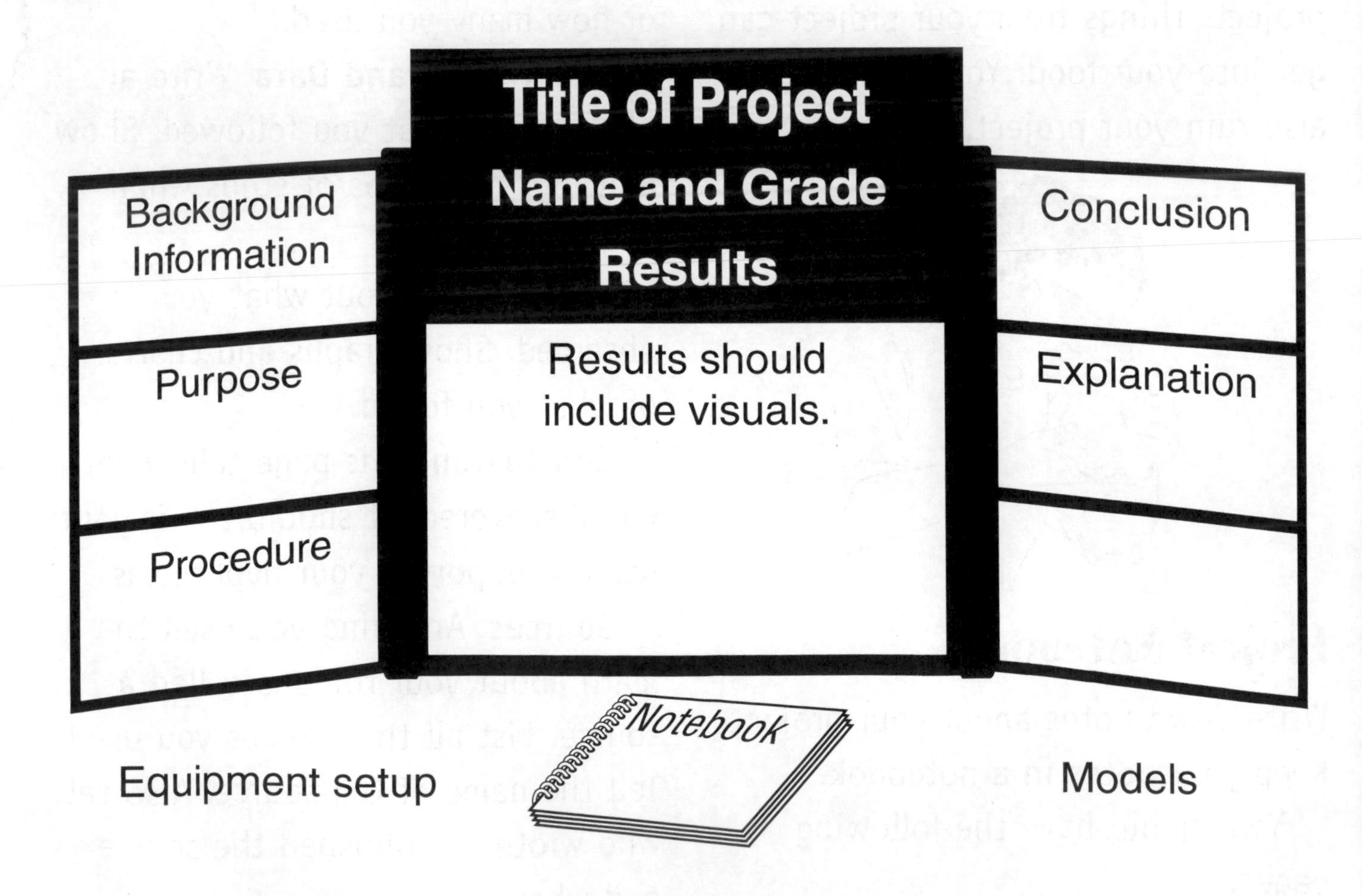

- **Does warm water freeze faster than cold water?** Find out how long it takes for water to freeze from different starting temperatures.
- **Is cold water heavier than warm water?** Use food coloring when adding warm water to cold water or cold water to warm water. The heavier one will sink in the other.
- **How does the mass of an object affect how far it goes?** Add weights to a toy car before letting it roll down a ramp. Measure the distance it travels.
- **How does the shape of an object affect how fast it can move through water or air?** Compare the motion of objects with different shapes. Show why submarines and cars are designed as they are.
- **How can steam make electricity?** Make a model of a power plant that uses steam.
- **What are the parts of a simple electric circuit?** Build a circuit that makes a light bulb turn on.
- **How can water be used to make electricity?** Make a model of a hydroelectric power plant.
- **How does a compass work?** Show how a compass points as it is moved around a bar magnet. Relate this to Earth as a magnet. Compare Earth's geographic and magnetic poles.
- **How can magnets make a train go?** Show how a maglev train works.
- **Why is the sky blue?** Show how sunlight splits light into colors to give the sky its color during the day and at sunset.
- **How can you use a pinhole camera?** Make and demonstrate the use of a pinhole camera.
- **Do different colors absorb heat differently?** Measure how the temperature of a substance changes when covered in different colors of paper or other material.
- **How does changing the conditions of a plant affect plant growth?** Turn a plant on its side or move it away from a window. Find out if the plant bends as a result.

- **Do plants grow better with different kinds of music?** Play different types of music for plants. Decide if some plants grow better than others.
- **Why do leaves change color in the fall?** Use paper chromatography to show that plant leaves have several colors in them. Show what happens when the green color disappears in the fall.
- **What organisms work together in nature?** Show how some organisms depend on each other in nature.
- **Do snails have color vision?** Try to determine if different colors affect snails.
- **How does mold grow?** Show what mold is and how it grows on foods. Compare how fast it grows on different types of foods.
- **What conditions affect how fast liquid water evaporates into a gas?** Compare how temperature, wind, and size affect this process.
- **What are the spheres of Earth and what is each made up of?** Make a model that shows Earth's lithosphere, atmosphere, hydrosphere, and biosphere.
- **How do fossils form?** Use clay and similar materials to show how fossils form.
- **What is a star?** Define a star and show its life cycle.
- **How can the sun cook foods?** Build a simple solar cooker and cook a potato.
- **How do seasons affect Earth?** Show how seasons cause changes around the planet.

Glossary

asteroid—a small, rocky object that orbits the sun (p. 94)

atom—the most basic part of matter (p. 7)

axis—an imaginary line that runs from the North Pole to the South Pole of Earth (p. 105)

battery—a device that stores electricity (p. 29)

cell—the basic unit of living things (p. 42)

circuit—a path through which electricity can flow (p. 29)

comet—a small amount of ice and dust that orbits the sun in a long path (p. 94)

community—all of the populations of organisms living in the same place (p. 66)

conduction—the flow of heat between objects that are touching each other (p. 29)

conductor—a material that lets thermal energy flow through it easily (p. 29)

convection—the movement of heat through liquids and gases (p. 29)

crater—a dent in the surface of the moon (p. 105)

delta—an area of land that forms when sediment is dropped at the mouth of a river (p. 82)

desert—an ecosystem that gets very little rain (p. 66)

distance—the length an object moves from a starting position (p. 20)

ecosystem—the living and nonliving things in an environment (p. 66)

energy—the ability to cause change (p. 29)

environment—everything around a living thing (p. 66)

erosion—the process through which natural forces, such as wind and water, carry away bits of rock and other materials over time (p. 82)

force—a push or a pull (p. 20)

forest—an area in which the main kinds of plants are trees (p. 66)

fresh water—water that does not have a lot of salt in it (p. 66)

gas—the state of matter that has no definite shape or size (p. 7)

germinate—the process through which a plant breaks out of a seed (p. 42)

grassland—an ecosystem made up of large, flat areas of land covered with grass (p. 66)

habitat—a part of an ecosystem where a population can get the things it needs (p. 66)

heat—the movement of thermal energy from a warmer object to a cooler one (p. 29)

igneous rock—rock that forms when lava or magma cools (p. 82)

insulator—a material that does not let thermal energy flow through it easily (p. 29)

life cycle—the changes that happen to an organism between birth and death (p. 55)

liquid—the state of matter that has a definite volume but takes the shape of its container (p. 7)

lunar eclipse—when the moon moves into Earth's shadow (p. 105)

magnet—an object that pulls materials, such as metals with iron, to it (p. 29)

mass—the amount of matter in an object (p. 7)

matter—any material or object that has mass and takes up space (p. 7)

metamorphic rock—rock that forms through changes in other rocks (p. 82)

metamorphosis—changes in the body and behavior of an organism (p. 55)

meteor—a piece of dust or rock that glows as it enters Earth's atmosphere (p. 94)

microscope—a tool that makes small things look bigger (p. 42)

mineral—a solid object that was formed in nature and has never been alive (p. 82)

motion—a change in the position of an object (p. 20)

orbit—the path an object follows as it travels around another object in space (p. 94)

organism—a living thing (p. 42)

phases—the changes in how the moon looks because of its motion around Earth (p. 105)

photosynthesis—the process through which plants make food (p. 42)

physical property—a characteristic of matter that can be found using the senses (p. 7)

planet—a large body of rock or gas that moves around a star (p. 94)

population—all of the same kind of organisms living in one area (p. 66)

radiation—the movement of heat without the use of matter (p. 29)

revolution—the movement of one object around another (p. 105)

rock—a solid object made of minerals (p. 82)

rock cycle—the process during which one type of rock changes into another (p. 82)

rotation—the spinning on an axis (p. 105)

salt water—water that has a lot of salt in it (p. 66)

sediment—bits of rock (p. 82)

sedimentary rock—rock that forms in layers from bits of rock (p. 82)

seedling—a young plant (p. 42)

soil—the loose material that plants need to grow (p. 82)

solar eclipse—when Earth moves into the moon's shadow (p. 105)

solar system—the sun and the objects that orbit it (p. 94)

solid—the state of matter that has a definite shape and takes up a definite amount of space (p. 7)

speed—the distance an object moves divided by the time during which it moves (p. 20)

star—a ball of glowing gases (p. 94)

thermal energy—the total energy of the particles in a sample of matter (p. 29)

volume—the amount of space an object or material takes up (p. 7)

weathering—the process through which rock is broken into small pieces (p. 82)

Answer Key

Assessment, pages 5–6

1. A 2. C 3. D 4. B
5. C 6. A 7. C 8. A
9. D 10. C 11. A 12. C

Unit 1 Lesson 1

Review, pp. 13–14

1. B 2. D 3. C
4. A 5. B 6. C
7. The particles are the same. However, they are close together and don't move very much in a solid. They can slide past each other in the liquid. They move far apart in a gas.
8. The mass tells how much matter is in it. The volume tells how much space it takes up.

All About Matter, p. 15

1. balance 2. gas
3. matter 4. physical
5. solid 6. taste
7. liquid 8. mass
9. atom 10. volume

Comparing Mass, p. 16

1. B 2. A 3. Same 4. A 5. B

Special Properties of Liquids, p. 17

1. Liquids form drops because their surfaces are pulled together.
2. The property is known as surface tension.
3. Like honey, molasses flows more slowly than water.

Experiment: Investigating Gases, pp. 18–19

Analysis

1. The gas went into the balloon.
2. It got bigger, or inflated.

Conclusion

Yes, they do. The gas took up space inside the balloon. As more gas was made, the balloon got bigger.

Unit 1 Lesson 2

Review, p. 22

1. B 2. A 3. D
4. B 5. D
6. A force is needed to start an object moving, to stop an object from moving, or to change an object's motion.
7. You need the distance it moves and the time it takes to move that distance.

Position, p. 23

1. penguin 2. biker
3. dog 4. car
5. airplane 6. space shuttle

Describing Motion, p. 24

Check student sentences. Each sentence should describe something that is moving. The first letter of the sentence should be the letter from the word MOTION.

The Alaskan Sled Race, pp. 25–26

1. C 2. B 3. B 4. D

Experiment: Investigating Motion, p. 28

Analysis

1. The distance moved stayed the same.
2. The speed at which I moved changed each time.
3. I moved the slowest during Walk 1 and the fastest during Walk 4.

Conclusion

The faster I move, the less time it takes to move a certain distance.

Unit 1 Lesson 3

Review, pp. 35–36

1. C **2.** A **3.** D
4. B **5.** C **6.** D

7. They start to move faster.

8. Different poles can be placed near each other so they pull together.

Finding Forms of Energy, p. 37

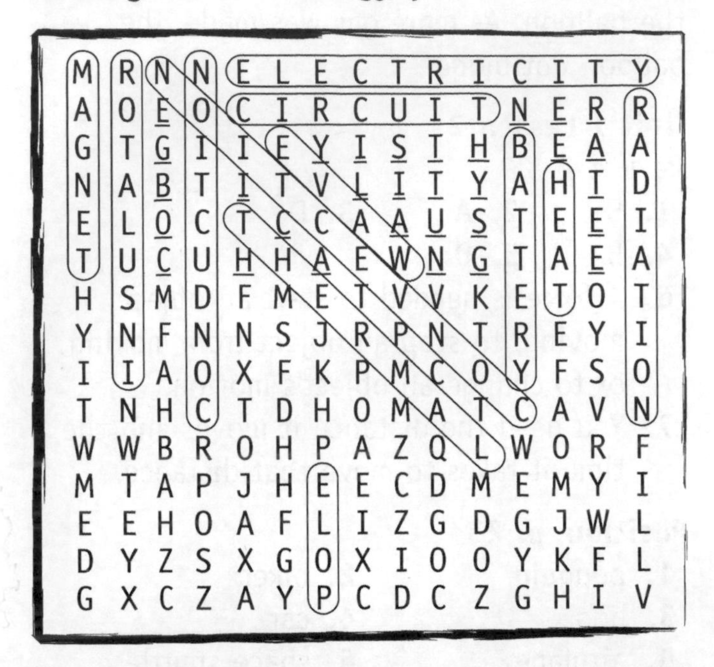

Secret message: Energy is the ability to cause change.

Heat Transfer, p. 38

1. radiation
2. conduction
3. convection

Electric Circuits, p. 39

1. battery
2. light bulb
3. wire
4. switch

Experiment: Investigating Light, pp. 40–41

Analysis

Students should draw straight lines to and from the wall at different angles.

Conclusion

1. It bounces straight back.
2. Yes, it bounces back at the same slant at which it hits the wall in the other direction.

Unit 2 Lesson 4

Review, pp. 49–50

1. A **2.** D **3.** C
4. B **5.** C **6.** C

7. Some seeds attach to their fur and are carried away. Others are eaten and dropped in new places.

8. It protects them from weather and from other animals.

Plant Parts, p. 51

1. leaf **2.** flower
3. stem **4.** roots

Single-Celled Organisms, p. 52

1. single **2.** microscope
3. Some **4.** moves

Experiment: Investigating the Needs of Plants, p. 54

Analysis

1. The control plant shows how the plant would grow with both water and sunlight.
2. Water and sunlight

Conclusion

No, the plants that did not get water or sunlight did not grow like the plant that got both.

Unit 2 Lesson 5

Review, pp. 58–59

1. B **2.** D **3.** C **4.** A **5.** B **6.** B

7. In one form, the adult form is very different from the young form. In the other, the adult form looks like a larger version of the young form.

8. The plant might make seeds or spores that make a new plant. The animal might reproduce to make more like itself.

Growing Up, p. 60
Check student posters. Encourage them to look for differences between the young and adults.

A Butterfly, p. 61
2, 1, 4, 3

The Emperor Penguin, p. 63
1. A **2.** B **3.** D **4.** C

Experiment: Investigating the Life Cycle of a Frog, p. 65
Analysis
1. They lost their tails and grew legs. They stopped swimming and climbed onto the rock.
2. They turned into frogs.
Conclusion
It begins as an egg that hatches into a tadpole. The tadpole changes into a frog.

Unit 2 Lesson 6
Review, pp. 73–74
1. B **2.** A **3.** C **4.** C **5.** B
6. A coastal forest forms in a cooler region than a tropical rain forest.
7. Rain brings fresh water to the surface. Rivers and streams bring fresh water to the coasts.

Forest Ecosystems, p. 75
1. canopy **2.** understory **3.** forest floor

All About Environments, p. 76
1. freshwater **2.** population
3. forest **4.** ecosystem
5. desert **6.** grassland
7. Deciduous **8.** community
9. saltwater **10.** habitat

Organisms and Where They Live, p. 77
1. ecosystem **2.** forest
3. desert **4.** community
5. population **6.** habitat
7. grassland **8.** freshwater
9. environment

Losing Ecosystems, pp. 78–79
1. C **2.** C **3.** B

Experiment: Investigating Environments, p. 81
Analysis
1. tropical rain forests
2. ocean
Conclusion
Warmer, wetter environments are near the equator. Colder, dryer environments are farthest from the equator.

Unit 3 Lesson 7
Review, p. 87
1. A **2.** D **3.** C **4.** B **5.** D
6. They write with them in pencils, they make objects out of them, they eat them, and they make jewelry out of them.
7. People need plants for food and oxygen. Plants need soil in order to live.

Earth's Materials, p. 88
1. igneous **2.** weathering
3. sediment **4.** soil
5. sedimentary **6.** metamorphic
7. rock **8.** erosion
9. cycle **10.** delta

Naming Earth's Materials, p. 89
1. erosion **2.** metamorphic rock
3. mineral **4.** weathering
5. igneous rock **6.** rock

The Hawaiian Islands, p. 91
1. C **2.** B **3.** D **4.** A

Experiment: Investigating Soil, p. 93
Analysis
1. This way I would know that the amount of water in the cup depended on the type of soil and not the amount of soil.
2. The grains of sand are larger.
3. The cup with the sand had the most water.

Conclusion
The potting soil absorbed more water. The larger the particles of the soil, the more easily water can pass through it.

Unit 3 Lesson 8
Review, pp. 98–99

1. D **2.** B **3.** C **4.** A **5.** B

6. They are mostly larger, made of frozen gas, colder, and farther from the sun.

7. Asteroids travel in an orbit between planets. Comets travel in long paths.

The Solar System, p. 100

1. planet **2.** asteroids
3. moon **4.** sun

Finding Objects in the Sky, p. 101

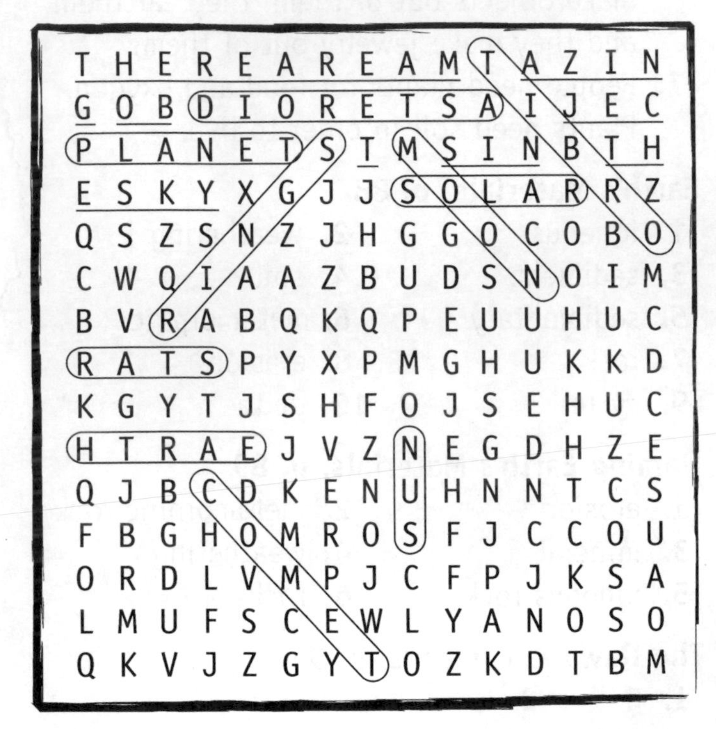

Hidden message:
There are amazing objects in the sky.

A New Way to Think About the Solar System, p. 102

1. C **2.** A **3.** A

Experiment: Investigating Models, p. 104
Analysis
No. All the planets orbit the sun in different positions. Mercury is the closest. Neptune is the farthest.
Conclusion
The solar system is very large and far away. Making models can help scientists study the solar system more easily on Earth.

Unit 3 Lesson 9
Review, pp. 109–110

1. C **2.** B **3.** A **4.** D **5.** A

6. No part of Earth would point toward the sun. The length of day and night would be the same. Temperatures would not be warm or cold. It would be like spring or fall all the time.

7. A lunar eclipse happens when Earth's shadow falls on the moon. A solar eclipse happens when the moon's shadow falls on Earth.

Changes in the Sky, p. 111

Across
3. moon
4. crater
5. orbit

Down
1. revolution
2. rotation

Seasons, p. 112

1. summer **2.** winter
3. winter **4.** summer

Calendars, p. 114

1. D **2.** C **3.** B **4.** A

Experiment: Investigating Seasons, p. 115
Analysis
The part of the globe with my town pointed toward the light.
Conclusion
The sunlight hits this place differently throughout Earth's orbit.

4500687231-0607-2017
Printed in the U.S.A